S0-AFG-309

THOMAS HARDY

The Return of the Native

Retold by Margaret Tarner

HEINEMANN

UPPER LEVEL

Series Editor: John Milne

The Heinemann Guided Readers provide a choice of enjoyable reading material for learners of English. The series is published at five levels – Starter, Beginner, Elementary, Intermediate and Upper. Readers at **Upper Level** are intended as an aid to students which will start them on the road to reading unsimplified books in the whole range of English literature. At the same time, the content and language of the Readers at **Upper Level** is carefully controlled with the following main features:

Information Control

As at other levels in the series, information which is vital to the development of a story is carefully presented in the text and then reinforced through the Points for Understanding section. Some background references may be unfamiliar to students, but these are explained in the text and in notes in the Glossary. Care is taken with pronoun reference.

Structure Control

Students can expect to meet those structures covered in any basic English course. Particularly difficult structures, such as complex nominal groups and embedded clauses, are used sparingly. Clauses and phrases within sentences are carefully balanced and sentence length is limited to a maximum of four clauses in nearly all cases.

Vocabulary Control

At **Upper Level**, there is a basic vocabulary of approximately 2,200 words. At the same time, students are given the opportunity to meet new words, including some simple idiomatic and figurative English usages which are clearly explained in the Glossary.

Glossary

The Glossary at the back of this book on page 87 is divided into 4 sections. A number beside a word in the text, like this [3], refers to a section of the Glossary. The words within each section are listed in alphabetical order. The page number beside a word in the Glossary refers to its first occurrence in the text.

Contents

The Return of
the Native

1

On Egdon Heath

It was a Saturday afternoon in early November – 5th November 1842. The day was ending. The sky over Egdon Heath was grey. The land below was dark.

Egdon Heath was wild, lonely and beautiful. People had always lived on Egdon Heath, but it had never changed.

The small, round hills of the heath climbed higher and higher, to the highest hill of all. This was Rainbarrow, the highest point on Egdon Heath. On top of this hill was an old burial-place[4] which had been there for hundreds of years.

A narrow road crossed the heath at its lowest point. A man was walking slowly along the road, leading a horse and van[2].

The man came slowly nearer. He was young and good-looking, but his face, clothes and hands were completely red. This strange traveller was a reddleman. He sold a red dye called reddle to the farmers who used it to mark their sheep. The reddleman was marked by the red dye too. His life was very lonely. All the children on the heath were afraid of this strange, red man.

The reddleman stopped after a time. He fed his horse and sat down by the side of his van. It was darker now. The reddleman looked across the heath. His eyes moved up its slopes to the highest hill of all, Rainbarrow.

A young woman was standing alone on the top of Rainbarrow. She was tall and she stood very still. Then suddenly, the woman turned and moved away. She was soon out of sight behind the hill.

As the reddleman watched, he saw other figures, climbing slowly to the top of Rainbarrow. They were all carrying wood. When they reached the top of the hill, they threw the wood onto the ground.

Very soon, a big fire was burning on Rainbarrow. As the reddleman turned his head, he could see other, smaller fires. On 5th November every year, the villagers of Egdon Heath lit these fires. It was an old custom[1]. Perhaps they were trying to forget the darkness of winter.

The reddleman stood up. It was almost night now. He brought out a lantern[2] from the van and lit it. The reddleman and his van moved slowly on.

2

Thomasin Comes Back Home

On the road below Rainbarrow stood an inn[1]. It was called the Quiet Woman. A light was shining from one window.

The reddleman and his van were now near the inn. Looking up, the reddleman saw an elderly[4] woman. She was hurrying along a path which led down to the road. The reddleman stopped his horse. He held up his lantern to see the woman's face.

'Aren't you Mrs Yeobright of Blooms-End, ma'am?' the reddleman called. 'Do you remember me?'

'You must be Diggory Venn, the reddleman,' Mrs Yeobright answered, coming nearer. 'I remember your father. What are you doing here, Reddleman, at this time of night?'

'I was on my way to see you, ma'am. I've something to tell you about your niece[4], Miss Thomasin. It's bad news, I'm afraid.'

'Bad news about Thomasin? Where is she?'

'Miss Thomasin's here in my van, ma'am,' the reddleman answered slowly.

'What new trouble is this?' Mrs Yeobright cried, putting her hand over her eyes. 'Thomasin went to Budmouth to get married. Where is her husband?'

'I don't know, ma'am. I was near Anglebury this morning. A short way out of the town, I heard someone following me. It was Miss Thomasin, as white as death. "Oh, Diggory Venn, please help me," she said. "I'm in trouble."

'And then she fainted. So I picked her up and put her in my van. She's in there now, asleep.'

The reddleman held up his lantern as Mrs Yeobright hurried up the steps of his van.

At the far end of the van lay a young girl, fast asleep. The light of the lantern shone on her sweet face and long, brown hair.

'Oh, Aunt!' cried Thomasin, sitting up. 'We couldn't get married. I am so unhappy.' And her soft, brown eyes filled with tears.

'Couldn't get married? Tamsin, Tamsin, what has happened?' Mrs Yeobright asked.

'I'll tell you everything, Aunt,' said the girl, standing up. 'Thank you, Reddleman, for bringing me home.'

When the two women were outside the van, Mrs Yeobright looked up at the dark sky. The fires on the hills were nearly all out now. Mrs Yeobright watched the reddleman's van move slowly down the road.

8

Then she turned to her niece and said angrily, 'Now, what is the meaning of this, Thomasin? Why are you alone?' Thomasin began to cry softly.

'It means that I am not married, Aunt,' she said. 'But it's nobody's fault[3].'

'Nobody's fault? What do you mean? I have never wanted you to marry Damon Wildeve. I have never liked him. But you went to Budmouth together. You must marry him now.'

'Mr Wildeve says we can marry in a day or two,' Thomasin answered.

'Then we'll go to the inn now and talk to him,' said Mrs Yeobright, looking across at the lighted window.

'Must I see him too, Aunt?' Thomasin asked.

'Of course you must. I don't trust[3] him to tell me the truth.'

Damon Wildeve was a young man from the big seaside town of Budmouth. He had not been successful there. He was now living on Egdon Heath. He was the landlord[4] of the Quiet Woman.

Mrs Yeobright and Thomasin walked through the open door of the inn. Mrs Yeobright knocked at a door at the end of a passage and went into the room.

Damon Wildeve was standing in front of the fire. He turned gracefully[4] to face the two women. He was a tall young man, with a handsome face. His thick, fair hair curled down over his neck.

'You've come home then, darling,' Wildeve said to Thomasin, who was standing behind her aunt. 'Why did you leave me like that?'

'I want to know why you and Thomasin are not married,' said Mrs Yeobright. 'Why have you disgraced[3] my niece, and me too?'

Mrs Yeobright was a proud woman. Although her dead husband had been a farmer, she had come from a good family[1]. Mrs Yeobright did not think that Damon Wildeve was good enough for her niece. At first, she had tried to stop the marriage, but then she had finally agreed to it.

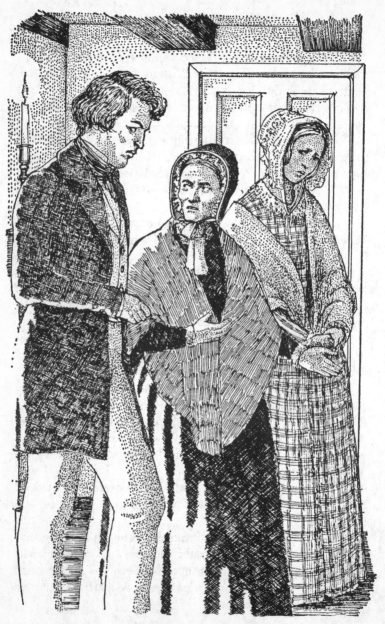

He was a tall young man, with a handsome face.

'Please sit down and I'll explain,' said Wildeve. 'It's no disgrace, only a stupid mistake. Thomasin and I planned to marry in Budmouth, then we changed our minds. We decided to go to Anglebury and get married there. I found out, too late, that we couldn't use the marriage licence[4] in Anglebury.'

'Then you are both to blame,' said Mrs Yeobright angrily. 'You have insulted[3] my family and everyone will laugh at Thomasin.'

Thomasin's large eyes looked from one face to another.

'Please leave us for five minutes, Aunt,' she said. 'I want to talk to Damon alone.'

'Of course, dear,' said Wildeve quickly. 'If your aunt will excuse us . . .'

'Oh, Damon, all this trouble is killing me,' Thomasin said sadly, when they were alone together. 'My aunt is so angry.'

'She is an unpleasant woman,' said Wildeve. 'I know she doesn't like me.'

'But what are we going to do, Damon?' Thomasin asked. 'You do want to marry me, don't you?'

'Of course I do. We can go to Budmouth on Monday and get married at once.'

'Then let us go. Oh, Damon,' Thomasin said, hiding her face. 'I am begging you to marry me! And I always dreamt that you would beg me to marry you.'

'Life is never like our dreams,' said Wildeve with a smile.

'Give me your hand, Damon,' Thomasin answered sadly.

As Wildeve took Thomasin carelessly by the hand, there was a loud knock at the back door. Wildeve went to answer it. When he came back a few minutes later, Thomasin and her aunt had gone.

Wildeve laughed quietly. Then he went to the front door and looked up at Rainbarrow. The big fire had gone out now. But as Wildeve turned his head, he saw a smaller fire. It was burning on a hill called Mistover Knap.

'You are calling me, are you, my lady?' Wildeve said quietly, as he looked at the fire.

11

About half an hour later, Wildeve left the inn, locking the doors carefully behind him. He stood for a moment, looking towards Mistover Knap.

'Yes, she is calling me. I must go to her, I suppose.'

And Wildeve began to walk quickly towards the fire.

3

The Meeting by the Fire

The tall young woman was standing again on Rainbarrow. She stood very still, listening. But all she could hear was the wind blowing across the heath.

After a time, the woman gave a sigh[3]. Far away down the valley, she could see a light. It was shining from the window of the Quiet Woman inn.

She brought out a small telescope[4] and looked through it. Then she looked at her watch. She had been waiting an hour. The woman sighed again.

Moving quickly, she began to follow a narrow path across the heath. She knew the way well. She was going towards the small, bright fire that Wildeve had seen from the inn.

The fire on Mistover Knap had been built high up on a bank which surrounded a house and garden. Behind the fire was a small pool.

The young woman walked quickly up the bank and looked at the bright fire. Sitting next to the fire was a small boy. From time to time, the boy threw a piece of wood on the fire.

The boy looked up at the dark-haired woman and said, 'I'm glad you have come back, Miss Eustacia. I don't like being here by myself.'

'You are a lucky boy to have a fire of your own,' the young woman replied. 'Has anyone been here while I've been away?'

'Only your grandfather, Miss. He's coming out now.' An old man was standing by the door of the house.

'When are you coming inside, Eustacia?' he asked. 'You are too old to be playing with fires. And you're burning my best wood.'

'It's Johnny's fire. He doesn't want to go yet,' Eustacia replied. 'Go to bed, Grandfather, I'll be in soon.'

The old man turned and went inside without a word.

'Now Johnny,' Eustacia said to the boy, 'if you stay a little longer, I'll give you a lucky sixpence. I'm going for a walk, but I'll be back soon. Put a piece of wood on the fire every two or three minutes. And if you hear a frog jump into the pool, run and tell me. It's a sign[4] of rain.'

'Yes, Eustacia.'

'You must call me Miss Vye.'

'Yes, Miss.'

Eustacia stood on the high bank and listened. It was a lonely place. She could see the whole valley, down to the stream behind Wildeve's inn. On the right, Rainbarrow rose up against the dark sky.

The young woman looked down at the heath impatiently. Twice, she went back to the fire.

'Has a frog jumped into the pool yet, Johnny?'

'No, Miss Eustacia,' the boy replied.

'Wait a little longer. Next time I come back, I'll give you the lucky sixpence.'

Eustacia went again to the end of the bank and stood with her back to the fire.

Suddenly the boy jumped up and ran towards her.

'A frog jumped into the pool, Miss. I heard it!'

'Then it is going to rain. Run home, now, Johnny. Here's your lucky sixpence. Run this way, through the garden. Hurry!'

Eustacia turned quickly back to the fire. She stood in silence, listening.

In a few moments, there was another splash in the pool. Eustacia moved nearer the fire.

'Yes?' she said quietly.

A man was standing on the other side of the pool. He climbed quickly up the bank and stood beside Eustacia. She laughed quietly. The man was Damon Wildeve.

'I have come,' he said. 'I knew your fire was for me.'

'You knew it was for you? But I have not spoken to you once since you chose her and left me.'

Eustacia turned away. Then she said, 'Yes, it was for you. You remembered our old sign⁴. You have not married Thomasin. You love me. That is why I called you.'

'How do you know I am not married?'

'My grandfather heard about it. You do love me, don't you?'

'If I didn't, I wouldn't be here now. God knows⁴, you have completely changed my life.'

Eustacia smiled and moved into the firelight. She took the shawl² away from her face and said, 'Have you ever in your life seen anything more beautiful than that?'

'No.'

'I am more beautiful than Thomasin.'

'Thomasin is a sweet and gentle woman,' Wildeve replied.

'Forget her, Damon,' Eustacia answered proudly. 'You have made me very unhappy,' she added. 'But perhaps I shall always be unhappy. I hate this wild heath. But at least you have come back to me.'

'Have I?' Wildeve said quietly. 'I came here tonight to say goodbye.'

'Thank you!' said Eustacia, turning away angrily. 'And I thought you loved me. I can never give myself to you again.'

'You have said that before, my sweet. And I have changed your mind. We'll meet again on Rainbarrow, as we used to.'

Wildeve moved nearer and held out his arms.

'Oh, no, don't kiss me!' Eustacia cried.

'Can I kiss your hand?'

'No.'

'Couldn't I hold your hand before I go?'

'No.'

'Goodnight then, Eustacia. Goodbye.'

In a moment, Wildeve had gone. Eustacia sighed and looked down at the dying fire. She knew that Wildeve did not love her. But she did not want to stop loving him. Who else could she love on Egdon Heath?

———

When she was ready for bed, Eustacia stood for a moment in front of her mirror. She saw a proud, beautiful woman, with dark hair and soft, white skin. Her eyes were large and very dark. Her lips were made to kiss.

Eustacia had only one desire – to be loved madly. But it was not easy to find love on Egdon Heath.

Egdon Heath was Eustacia's prison. She had grown up in the

seaside town of Budmouth. There, she had been gay and happy. Then her father and mother had died. Eustacia went to live with her grandfather, Captain Vye. When the Captain bought the lonely house on Egdon Heath, Eustacia had to live there too.

Every day, Eustacia walked alone on Egdon Heath. She dreamt of a love that would change her life. She was waiting for a man who would love her and take her away from the heath forever. She dreamt of living with him in Paris, the centre of the fashionable world.

Eustacia turned away from the mirror with a sigh and put out the candle. In a few minutes, she was in bed and asleep.

4

A Meeting on Rainbarrow

As soon as Johnny had left the fire, he began to run, holding his lucky sixpence tightly. He was a little afraid of Eustacia and he was glad to be going home.

Then, suddenly, the boy stopped. There was a strange, red light in front of him. There was red dust too, and a loud noise.

The boy was afraid to pass the red light alone. He turned slowly back to Mistover Knap. Perhaps Miss Vye would let her servant walk home with him.

The fire on the bank was still burning. But now two figures were standing beside it. One was Eustacia, the other, a man. The boy listened for a few minutes. He knew that Eustacia would be angry if she saw him. With a sigh, the boy went back the way he had come.

The light and the dust had gone. Near a deep opening in the

side of the hill, was a horse. The boy was not afraid of that. But inside the opening was a van. And inside the van sat a man who was red from head to foot. It was Diggory Venn, the reddleman.

At that moment, the reddleman stood up and came out of his van. He had his lantern in his hand and its light shone on his eyes and his white teeth.

Full of fear, the boy made a sudden movement. Unable to stop himself, he rolled down the slope to the reddleman's feet.

'Who are you?' asked the reddleman quickly.

'Johnny Nunsuch, master²!'

'What are you doing here?'

'I was coming home from Miss Vye's fire,' the boy answered.

'You have hurt your hand,' said the reddleman more kindly. 'Let me tie it up for you.'

'Please let me look for my sixpence. I've dropped it.'

'A sixpence? Who gave you that?' Venn asked.

'Miss Vye did, for looking after her fire.'

The reddleman said nothing, but tied up the boy's hand and found his sixpence.

'Thank you, master, I must go home now,' said the boy.

'You're afraid of the reddleman, aren't you?' Venn said. 'I suppose all children are.'

'Not so much now, master,' the boy replied. 'Were you making the red light I saw before?'

'Yes, I was shaking out my empty reddle bags. Tell me, why did Miss Vye want a fire? I saw it burning up there.'

'I don't know,' Johnny answered. 'She made me sit by it while she went to Rainbarrow. When a frog jumped into the pool, she sent me home.'

'Frogs don't jump into pools at this time of year,' the reddleman said slowly.

'They do, I heard one. Miss Vye told me I would.'

'And what happened then?' asked the reddleman.

'I came here and I was afraid of the red light. So I went back to

Miss Eustacia. But a gentleman was with her. They didn't see me, master.'

'A gentleman with Miss Vye! Did you hear what they said?' the reddleman asked.

Johnny told the reddleman what he had heard.

So they meet on Rainbarrow, do they? the reddleman said to himself. Then he took Johnny back to the path. And the boy ran off.

When he was alone, the reddleman sat for a time, looking into his fire. Then he stood up and went into his van. He came out with a letter in his hand. The letter was two years old and it had been opened and read many times. The letter was from Thomasin Yeobright. She had written:

Dear Diggory Venn,

I was very surprised at your question. I'm afraid I can't marry you. I'm sorry I laughed when you asked me. My aunt likes you. But I'm sure she doesn't want me to marry a dairy-farmer[1] like you. It is better if we don't meet again.

Thomasin Yeobright.

18

Diggory Venn had not seen Thomasin again until that morning. Soon after he received the letter, Venn had become a reddleman. This strange young man now spent his life wandering alone on Egdon Heath.

Venn loved Thomasin and he wanted her to be happy. He made up his mind. He would listen to Eustacia and Wildeve the next time they met on Rainbarrow.

———

Venn watched on Rainbarrow for a week, but nobody came. Then one evening, he saw a man and woman near his hiding-place. The first sound the reddleman heard was Eustacia crying.

'You are asking me whether you should marry Thomasin,' she was saying. 'Marry her if you like. I don't care. But you don't love her. You want me again, you know you do.'

'Tamsie is a good woman, that's the trouble,' said Wildeve. 'I wish I could go on meeting you without hurting her. But I can't.'

'I am nothing to you!' Eustacia cried. 'Nothing!'

'Nothing? Don't you remember last year, Eustacia – when we walked together on the heath? We loved each other then.'

'Did we? And do you love me now? Tell me.'

'I do and I don't,' said Wildeve with a smile. 'Sometimes I find you perfect, sometimes I like Thomasin better.'

Eustacia stood in silence. Then she said, 'I am going to walk this way. You will follow me, I know. You would marry me tomorrow if you could.'

'So I would,' said Wildeve. 'How I hate this heath! I know you hate it too. Listen to the wind!'

Eustacia shivered.

'One day I'll die here,' she said. 'I know it.'

The two lovers looked across the dark countryside.

'God, how lonely it is!' said Wildeve. He hurried to face Eustacia and took her hands in his. 'Why do we stay here? Come with me to America,' he said suddenly. 'I have relatives there. Let us go there together and leave this terrible place.'

'America?' Eustacia repeated slowly. 'Would I be happy there? You must give me time to think, Damon.'

As she spoke, Eustacia moved away and Wildeve followed her.

The reddleman came out of his hiding-place and walked slowly back to his van.

'My poor Tamsie,' he said at last. 'I must help her, I must!'

5

Tamsie's Friends Try To Help Her

The conversation Venn had heard between Eustacia and Wildeve had made him unhappy. He was still in love with Thomasin and he wanted to save her from unhappiness. He decided that he must talk to Eustacia Vye alone.

Eustacia and her grandfather had very few visitors. When the reddleman called at the house, he had to wait outside. Eustacia kept him waiting for nearly twenty minutes.

Venn had never spoken to Eustacia before. He soon realised that she was proud and clever. She was very different from the simple country girl, Thomasin Yeobright.

Eustacia was very angry when the reddleman began to talk about Wildeve. She was even more angry when Venn told her how he had listened on Rainbarrow. When Venn asked Eustacia to stop meeting Wildeve, she refused. Eustacia had no wish to make Thomasin happy.

'I am going indoors now,' Eustacia said at last. 'I have nothing more to say to you. You must have work to do, Reddleman. Why don't you go and do it?'

When Diggory Venn had left her, Eustacia stood looking down the valley. She could see the Quiet Woman inn, Damon Wildeve's home.

'I will never give him up – never!' the proud girl said at last.

————

Mrs Yeobright was also trying to help her niece. She had decided to speak to Wildeve about a new date for the marriage.

Mrs Yeobright saw the reddleman as she was on her way to the Quiet Woman. Venn was walking slowly back from Captain Vye's house, thinking about his conversation with Eustacia.

They stopped when they met. Venn immediately began to speak. He told Mrs Yeobright that he had asked Thomasin to marry him two years before.

Mrs Yeobright looked at the reddleman in surprise.

'I wasn't red then, you know,' Venn told her. 'But Thomasin thought you would object to our marriage. I think you may change your mind now I have as much money as Wildeve. And I won't be a reddleman forever.'

Mrs Yeobright noticed for the first time that Diggory Venn was young and good-looking. Then she shook her head.

'Thomasin thinks she ought to marry Wildeve,' she said. 'And I think so too, after what has happened. Thank you for your help, Reddleman, but there is nothing else to be done.'

Mrs Yeobright walked into the Quiet Woman. She thought of what she should say to Damon Wildeve. She didn't like Damon, but she understood him. Her first words were to warn him that the reddleman wanted to marry Thomasin.

Wildeve was very surprised and angry too.

'But I am going to marry Thomasin,' he said.

'I have heard that before,' Mrs Yeobright answered.

'Now, Mrs Yeobright, I don't want to quarrel with you,' Wildeve replied smiling pleasantly. 'We both want Thomasin to be happy. I will think about what you have said. We can talk about this again in a day or two.'

Mrs Yeobright agreed. She went home feeling sure that Wildeve would marry her niece.

But Wildeve was still undecided. Which woman did he love? Eustacia or Thomasin?

That night, Wildeve met Eustacia again. Once again he asked her to go away with him to America. He told her that she had one week to make up her mind. Would she agree to leave Egdon Heath with him, or not?

Eustacia went back to the house feeling very unhappy. She understood Wildeve perfectly. He only wanted her again because he was afraid of losing Thomasin!

Captain Vye was at home. He had just returned from his usual evening visit to the Quiet Woman.

'Have you heard the latest news, Eustacia?' he asked. 'Young Clym Yeobright is coming home next week. He is Mrs Yeobright's son. He is coming back to spend Christmas with his mother. He's a fine young man and a clever one too.'

'I have never heard of him before,' said Eustacia. 'Where has he been living all this time?'

22

'In Paris. He's done very well for himself there.'

Eustacia was immediately interested in Clym Yeobright, but she asked no more questions about him. Her mind was full of what her grandfather had told her.

A clever young man was returning to Egdon Heath from Paris. To Eustacia, Clym Yeobright was a man coming from Heaven.

Perhaps, she thought to herself, he is the man I have been waiting for all my life!

6

Clym Yeobright's Return

About a week before Christmas, Eustacia took her usual afternoon walk on the heath. It was the day that Clym Yeobright was returning to Egdon.

Eustacia longed[3] to see Clym and so she walked towards Mrs Yeobright's house at Blooms-End.

But to the girl's disappointment, there were no lights in the house. She could hear no sounds of life. After waiting for about ten minutes, Eustacia turned sadly and walked back towards Mistover Knap.

But Eustacia had not gone far when she saw three people coming towards her in the evening darkness. Eustacia moved a little way from the path to let them pass.

As the two women and the man walked by, the man called out, 'Goodnight!'

Eustacia did not answer. But she had recognised Mrs Yeobright and Thomasin. The man with them must be Clym Yeobright. Eustacia had not seen his face. But the man from Paris had spoken to her!

Eustacia hurried back to her grandfather's house.

'Why aren't we friendly with the Yeobrights?' she asked him. 'They seem to be nice people. Mrs Yeobright comes from a good family, I believe. They are not village people.'

'That's true, I suppose,' Captain Vye answered. 'But the Yeobrights have always lived in a very simple way. We never meet, because I said something, long ago, that made Mrs Yeobright angry. She has not spoken to me since.'

For the rest of that week, Eustacia took her walk near Blooms-End, but she did not see Clym Yeobright again.

On the evening of 23rd December, two days before Christmas, Eustacia was at home alone. She had heard that Clym Yeobright was not staying long on Egdon Heath.

Of course he will go soon, Eustacia told herself sadly. Who would choose to live on Egdon Heath if he could live in Paris? He will go back and I shall never see him.

At that moment, there was a knock at the door. Eustacia recognised the villager who was standing there.

'What do you want, Charley?' she asked the young man.

'Please, Miss Eustacia, your grandfather said we could practise⁴ in his barn⁴,' Charley answered.

'Oh, yes, of course. You are the mummers¹,' Eustacia said. 'There is the key. Do as you like.'

Every Christmas, for hundreds of years, the villagers of Egdon Heath had acted the old mummers' play of Saint George and the Turkish Knight. Only the men took part in the play. The women made the costumes¹, which became finer and more colourful every year. The play was acted in different houses on different nights.

As Eustacia sat by the fire, she could hear the voices of the mummers repeating their words. Tired of sitting alone, the young woman went out to the barn and looked through a small hole in the wall.

The villagers had finished their practice now and were talking together.

24

'Have you all got your costumes ready, lads?' one asked.

'We'll be ready by Monday,' they replied.

'That's the first night – at Mrs Yeobright's,' one added.

'Mrs Yeobright?' asked another. 'Why are we going there? Why does a lady like Mrs Yeobright want to see our old play?'

'She's having a party for her son, Clym. He hasn't spent Christmas at home for a long time. She wants everyone to be there.'

'Of course, I'd forgotten about the party.'

Eustacia had heard enough to make her unhappy. There was to be a party for Clym Yeobright, but she hadn't been invited. She walked slowly back to the house.

Eustacia was sitting by the fire again when Charley came back with the key to the barn.

Eustacia pointed to a chair and said, 'Sit there for a minute, Charley. I want to talk to you. You are taking the part of the Turkish Knight, aren't you? Would you say your words to me? I should like to hear them.'

Charley smiled and began. Eustacia had heard the words many times before. When Charley had finished, Eustacia repeated the words without a mistake.

'Well, you are a clever lady,' said Charley in surprise. 'You can say the words better than me!'

'Would you let me play your part for one night?' Eustacia asked softly.

'But women can't be mummers!'

'I would wear boys' clothes under my costume. No one would know me. I want to take your place on Monday night. Tell the others I'm your cousin. Now Charley, how much must I give you to let me do this?'

'I don't want money, Miss,' Charley replied quickly. 'But I'll do it if you let me hold your hand in mine.'

Eustacia was very surprised. But she said at last, 'Very well. You can hold my hand for fifteen minutes. Bring me your costume

25

tomorrow, Charley, and I will let you hold my hand then.'

The next day, when Charley brought the costume, Captain Vye was not at home. Eustacia went to her room and put on the brightly coloured clothes and the helmet[1]. Her face was completely covered by the ribbons which hung from the helmet.

'Now listen,' Eustacia said when she came downstairs. And she repeated her part again without a mistake.

Charley told Eustacia the time the mummers were meeting on the Monday evening. Then he was allowed to hold Eustacia's hand for fifteen minutes.

Eustacia felt happy and excited. She wasn't thinking of the young boy who was holding her hand. She was thinking of the moment when she would see Clym Yeobright. Eustacia had something to do, something to look forward to at last.

The fifteen minutes ended and Charley was sent home. Eustacia sat down by the fire. She tried to imagine the face of the man she was already half in love with.

7

The Mummers' Play

On Monday evening, Eustacia put on her costume and went to meet the mummers. Charley had told them that his cousin was taking his place that night. The mummers could not see Eustacia's face and they thought that she was a boy. They all set off together across the heath to Blooms-End.

There was a moon that night, but the heath was as dark and strange as ever. It was cold and the mummers walked quickly. After about half an hour, they could hear the sounds of music and dancing from Mrs Yeobright's house.

The mummers waited outside the house until the dancing

Eustacia put on her costume.

had finished. Only one door separated Eustacia from the man she had come to see. The music stopped, and at once the mummer who was dressed as Father Christmas knocked on the door with his heavy stick.

'Ah, the mummers, the mummers!' cried several voices, as the door opened. All the guests sat down at one end of the room and the old play began.

When Eustacia's turn came, she walked boldly into the middle of the room and spoke her words well. At last came the fight between Saint George and the Turkish Knight. The Turkish Knight fell to the floor – dead. Eustacia's part was over. For the first time, she could look at the face of the man she had come to see.

A pleasant-looking man of about thirty, with a thoughtful, intelligent face, was standing at the end of the room. Eustacia had never seen him before and she knew that this must be Clym Yeobright. The girl looked at him eagerly, trying to find out what kind of man he was.

The play was soon over and Mrs Yeobright invited the mummers to eat and drink. Eustacia got up and stood with the others. But now she found herself in a difficulty. If she took off her helmet to eat, everyone would recognise her. So when Clym Yeobright offered her some food, Eustacia shook her head.

'Surely you will eat something?' Clym Yeobright asked kindly.

'Nothing, thank you,' Eustacia replied, looking down at the ground.

When the girl spoke, Clym looked at her thoughtfully, but he said nothing. He went over to speak to his cousin, Thomasin, who was sitting sadly by herself. Eustacia remembered something she had heard. When Clym Yeobright was a boy, he had been half in love with his pretty cousin.

All at once, Eustacia was wildly jealous. She wanted to show herself as a beautiful and interesting woman. But she was in the

Clym looked at her thoughtfully.

Yeobrights' house as a mummer and must keep her face covered. Why had she come?

A few moments later, Clym Yeobright again came up to where Eustacia was sitting. He looked at her as though he wanted to ask her a question.

Eustacia had to escape. She got up quietly and went outside the house. Then the door opened again and Clym Yeobright stood beside her.

'I should like to ask you a question,' he said. 'I think you are a woman. Am I right?'

'I am a woman,' replied Eustacia softly.

'But girls don't play as mummers, do they?' Clym asked. 'Why did you do it?'

'To find some excitement. To make myself less sad.'

'What makes you sad?'

'Life.'

'I could have asked you to the party,' Clym said kindly. 'Did I ever meet you when I lived here before?'

'No, never,' Eustacia answered sadly.

'Then this is a strange first meeting. But I will ask you no more questions.'

Eustacia said nothing and Clym went back into the house.

Eustacia was now too excited to wait for the other mummers. She walked home quickly. She kept repeating to herself every word that Clym Yeobright had said to her.

She had met this man as she had planned, and he had spoken to her. But how would she ever meet him again? She was a complete stranger to the Yeobright family.

When she reached Mistover Knap, Eustacia stood for a moment. She looked up at Rainbarrow and the bright moon above it. And then she remembered.

This was the night she had promised to meet Damon Wildeve. She was to tell him whether or not she would go away with him.

'Well, it's too late now. He has his answer,' Eustacia said

aloud. Then she thought again of Clym Yeobright, living in the same house as his pretty cousin, Thomasin.

'How I wish she was safely married to Damon!' Eustacia cried. 'And it is my fault that she is not. If only I had known!'

———

Before she went to sleep that night, Eustacia wrote Wildeve a letter. She sent it to him the following day with the few small presents he had given her.

Wildeve read Eustacia's words with the greatest surprise.

After thinking it over carefully, I have decided that we must not meet or speak to each other again. For two years now, you have been unfaithful[3] to me. I am ending our friendship because you are marrying another woman.

Eustacia.

'I have been made a fool of!' said Wildeve angrily.

Two days later, Wildeve and Thomasin were married. Eustacia was in the church and Wildeve turned pale when he saw her. His look seemed to say: 'I have punished you now.'

In reply to his look, Eustacia had answered quietly, 'You are wrong. It gives me the greatest pleasure to see you married to Thomasin today.'

8

Clym's Plan

Clym Yeobright loved Egdon Heath. To Clym, the heath was a place of life and beauty at every season of the year. When Clym Yeobright walked on the heath, he was never lonely. He loved to be near the birds, animals and plants that made the heath beautiful for him. Clym loved the heath as much as Eustacia hated it.

At first, Clym had planned to stay at Blooms-End for only two weeks. But he became more and more unwilling to return to Paris where he was the manager of a large diamond[4] company. Clym had worked hard there for several years and had reached a good position.

But Clym had never forgotten the quiet life of Egdon Heath. Now as he walked about the heath again and spoke to the people who lived there, Clym made a new plan.

Mrs Yeobright wondered why Clym was staying with her so long. But she was too proud to ask her son any questions. One Sunday morning, Clym told his mother about his plan.

'I am not going back to Paris, Mother,' he said. 'I have given up my job there and sent for all my things.'

'Why didn't you tell me this before, Clym?' Mrs Yeobright asked in surprise.

'I should have told you, I know,' Clym answered. 'But I didn't think you would be pleased with my plan.'

'I don't think I am. What is this plan? Why do you want to leave the good job you have in Paris?'

'I want to help people,' Clym told his mother. 'Selling diamonds helps no one but myself. I want to help poor people. To do this in the way I want to, I must become a school-master . . .'

Mrs Yeobright was angry. She loved her son and was very proud of him. She wanted him to be a success.

'You would be wasted[4] as a schoolmaster,' Mrs Yeobright said. 'Why give up your good position in the world? There are plenty of schoolmasters.'

Clym did not answer.

As Mrs Yeobright and her son sat in unhappy silence, there was a knock on the door.

A villager who sometimes helped Mrs Yeobright with her garden hurried into the room. He was a silly young man whose name was Christian Cantle.

'Such a strange thing happened in church today,' Christian began. 'We were all praying and the church was quiet. Then suddenly, someone gave a terrible scream.'

'Why, what happened?' Mrs Yeobright asked. 'Who screamed?'

'It was Miss Vye,' Christian Cantle answered. 'She screamed because Susan Nunsuch had pushed a long needle into her arm!'

'How terrible!' Mrs Yeobright cried. 'Why did Susan do that?'

'Susan Nunsuch thinks Miss Vye is a witch[1], ma'am. She says

Miss Vye has made her son, Johnny, ill. Then Miss Vye fainted and everybody began to scream! What a sad thing for a beautiful young woman like Miss Vye!'

When Christian Cantle had gone, Clym looked at his mother.

'These are the people I must teach,' he told her. 'How can they believe in witches? This is a terrible thing to have happened.'

'Good girls are not called witches,' Mrs Yeobright said sharply.

'Who is Miss Vye?' Clym asked.

'She is a proud girl from Budmouth,' his mother answered. 'She walks on the heath by herself and talks to nobody.'

Early that afternoon, some villagers called at Mrs Yeobright's house to borrow some strong rope. They explained that Captain Vye's bucket[2] had fallen into his well. The rope had broken and it was impossible to get water.

Clym found the rope for them and then said, 'Is Captain Vye related to Miss Vye who was so badly treated this morning?'

'That's right. He's her grandfather,' one of the villagers answered. 'Miss Vye's such a pretty girl, Mr Clym. You ought to see her.'

'And she's clever too,' added another.

'Do you think Miss Vye would like to teach children?' Clym asked slowly.

'I don't know, sir. You should ask her. She's clever enough, I'm sure.'

'I'm afraid our two families are not very friendly,' Clym answered.

'Then why don't you come to Mistover Knap with us tonight?' the man said. 'We are going to get the bucket out of Captain Vye's well at six o'clock. Miss Vye is sure to be there. And you could help us too.'

'I'll think about it,' Clym replied and he went back into the house. He had an idea that the Turkish Knight and this beautiful girl were the same person – Eustacia Vye.

34

9

The Meeting at the Well

The afternoon was fine and Clym walked on the heath with his mother for an hour.

They reached the high point where the Quiet Woman and Mistover Knap could both be seen. Mrs Yeobright had decided to visit Thomasin in her new home.

'Then I'll leave you here,' Clym told his mother. 'I am going to Mistover Knap. I can help the villagers to get Captain Vye's bucket out of the well. And I would like to see Miss Vye too. I want to talk to her.'

'Must you go?' Mrs Yeobright asked sadly.

'Yes,' Clym answered quietly.

Mrs Yeobright watched her son as he walked quickly towards Mistover Knap.

They were sure to meet some time, she told herself unhappily. Clym will become interested in Eustacia Vye and he will feel sorry for her. And then what will happen?

With a sigh, Mrs Yeobright turned back to Blooms-End. She was too unhappy to visit Thomasin now.

Meanwhile, Clym hurried on to Mistover Knap, his long shadow stretching out in front of him.

When Clym got there, the villagers were already trying to get the bucket out of the deep well.

The bucket was nearly at the top now. Hands stretched out to catch it. Then with a crash, it fell back into the well again.

When the next try was made, Clym knelt by the well with the rope in his hands.

'Tie a rope round him, it's dangerous!' a voice cried. It was Eustacia Vye. Everyone turned to look at her. The beautiful girl

35

was leaning from an upper window. The glass of the window was red with the setting sun.

The work went on and after a time a villager took Clym's place. As soon as Clym heard the girl's voice he knew that the Turkish Knight and Eustacia Vye were the same person.

At last the bucket was brought up, but it had a great hole in the bottom. Eustacia came to the door of the house and said sadly, 'I can have no water tonight then . . .'

'I can send some water over from Blooms-End,' said Clym, stepping forward.

'Thank you, it doesn't matter,' Eustacia answered. 'My grandfather says we have water. I'll show you.'

As the villagers left Mistover Knap, Eustacia took Clym to the small pool beyond the bank. The ashes of the fire could still be seen.

Eustacia dropped a stone into the water of the little pool.

'Can I drink that?' she asked, with a smile.

'The water looks clean enough, I think,' Clym answered.

'No,' said Eustacia. 'I can try to live on this deserted heath. But I cannot drink water from a pool.'

In answer, Clym turned back to the well. He asked Eustacia to hold the rope. He thought he could bring up a little water in a smaller bucket.

Eustacia took hold of the rope, but it slipped through her fingers.

'Are you hurt?' Clym asked as Eustacia cried out.

Eustacia held out her hands. One of them was bleeding where the rope had dragged off the skin.

'You should have let go.' Clym told her gently.

'But you told me to hold on. This is the second time I have been hurt today. Look!'

And Eustacia pulled back her sleeve. She showed Clym the bright red mark on her arm.

'It was bad of that woman,' Clym said. He looked at the mark on Eustacia's white arm as though he would like to kiss it.

'The people here need education,' Clym said. 'And that is my plan for them. Would you help me to teach them? Together, we could do a lot.'

'Could we? Sometimes I feel I hate these people. But I should like to hear your ideas.'

Clym stood for a moment and then said, 'I think we have met before. But I did not see your face then.'

'Perhaps,' Eustacia replied.

'You are lonely here,' Clym added gently.

'I hate this heath,' Eustacia answered. 'I feel that it is a prison.'

'A prison?' Clym repeated in surprise. 'I love Egdon Heath at all times of the year. Even now when it is hard and dark. I would rather live on these hills than anywhere else in the world.'

'And yet you have lived in Paris! How I long for the life of a great city!'

'I used to think that too,' Clym answered. 'But five years of city life have changed my mind.'

Eustacia smiled sadly.

'I must go inside now, Mr Yeobright, and put a bandage[4] on my hand,' she said.

As Eustacia moved about the house that evening, she felt that a new life was beginning for her. The future seemed exciting and full of good things.

Clym walked across the dark heath, his thoughts full of his teaching plans. And now a beautiful woman was a part of them.

Clym spent the rest of the evening unpacking his books. In the morning, he got up early while it was still dark. He read for two hours by the light of his lamp. He studied all day until the late afternoon. Then he walked on the heath, in the direction of Mistover Knap.

As he hoped, he met Eustacia there.

10

Love Grows

In the new year, Clym continued to study. He worked and read for many hours every day.

Clym also walked on the heath. His walks were often in the direction of Mistover Knap or Rainbarrow.

Mrs Yeobright watched her son, but asked him no questions. She could see now that he was determined to be a schoolmaster. She also guessed that Clym and Eustacia often met on the heath. Mrs Yeobright became angry and jealous. She spoke to her son less and less.

The year went on. The month of March arrived and Egdon Heath began to wake from its winter sleep. The growing plants covered the heath with a light, clear green.

One fine spring evening, Clym met Eustacia by the pool on Mistover Knap. They stood there together and kissed for the first time. Clym returned to his mother's house full of joy. His face was flushed[3] and his eyes were bright with happiness.

Mrs Yeobright had already prepared the evening meal. Clym sat down opposite his mother as usual. At first, he took no notice of her silence. Then he spoke.

'For five days, we have eaten our meals in silence, Mother. What is the use of it?'

'No use, I suppose,' Clym's mother replied, 'but you know my reason.'

'The reason for your anger and your silence is Eustacia Vye. I know that,' Clym answered.

'And I know that you meet her and that you are wasting your life because of her. If it wasn't for her, you would have given up your plans long ago. You would be back in Paris by now.'

'That is not true, Mother,' Clym replied. 'I am determined to start a school. Eustacia Vye is an educated woman. She could help me with my work.'

'She will be no help to you,' Mrs Yeobright answered. 'Eustacia Vye is a lazy, unhappy woman. She has no interest in helping people. She thinks too much about herself.'

'I don't agree, Mother,' Clym answered. 'Eustacia could look after the pupils of a boarding school. I could teach them and go on studying for my own examinations. With a wife like her . . .'

'A wife? Then you mean to marry her? Oh, Clym, your love has blinded you! Eustacia Vye is not a good woman. I must save you from this foolishness!'

Clym stood up angrily.

'I cannot stay here when you speak like that about Eustacia,' he said.

In a few minutes, Clym had left the house. When he returned, several hours later, his mother had already gone to bed.

The next day was an unhappy one at Blooms-End. Clym Yeobright spoke to his mother, but she refused to answer. He worked until seven o'clock, then put on his coat and left the house.

Clym was meeting Eustacia on Rainbarrow that night. He waited for a few minutes and then heard Eustacia's light footstep. In a moment, she was in his arms and his lips were on hers.

'My Eustacia!'

'Clym, dearest,' she replied.

Three months had passed and now the two were deeply in love.

Eustacia sighed.

'Ah, Clym, we shall not always love like this!'

'Why do you say that?' Clym, cried, holding Eustacia in his arms.

'Because I know more about love than you do, Clym,' Eustacia answered sadly. 'I loved another man once, and now I love you.'

'Don't speak like that, Eustacia, for God's sake!'

'Well, I shall not be the first one to stop loving,' said Eustacia. 'Your mother will soon find out about our meetings. Then she will turn you against me.'

'My mother knows already,' said Glym sadly.

'And she hates me, I suppose?'

Clym did not answer.

'Kiss me once more then!' Eustacia cried, 'and leave me forever!'

'I will never leave you,' Clym answered. 'I came here tonight to ask you to be my wife. Will you marry me, Eustacia? You must give me an answer.'

'Let me think about it,' said Eustacia softly. 'Tell me more about Paris, Clym. I love to hear about those busy streets, those beautiful buildings . . .'

'Never mind[4] Paris,' Clym answered. 'Will you marry me, Eustacia?'

'If you take me back to Paris with you – I'll marry you at once,' Eustacia replied.

'Both you and my mother want me to go back to Paris!' Clym exclaimed. 'But I can't. My work is here, as a schoolmaster.'

'That plan will never come true, I am sure,' Eustacia said with a smile. 'So I promise to be yours for ever and ever. But whether I'll make you a good wife, I can't say. I do love you, Clym. To be your wife and to live in Paris would be heaven for me. But I love you so much that I will live with you here on Egdon Heath.'

Hand in hand, they walked back to Mistover. Eustacia promised that she would speak to her grandfather about their decision to marry. Then the lovers parted and Clym walked on to Blooms-End.

As he walked further away from Eustacia, Clym's thoughts grew sadder.

Did Eustacia really believe he would take her to Paris? Was that the only reason she loved him? Clym was also beginning to see that his love for Eustacia was turning him away from his mother.

Clym wanted to keep Eustacia's love, but he wanted the love

41

of his mother too. He also planned to become a teacher. He now realised that he could not have these three desires together. He reached home, worried and unhappy.

11

Clym Makes up his Mind

During the next few months, Clym and Eustacia continued to meet in secret. When Clym was not with Eustacia, he was studying hard.

One afternoon, Mrs Yeobright came home from a visit to Thomasin.

'I have heard something very strange,' she told Clym. 'Captain Vye has been talking at the Quiet Woman. He says that you and Eustacia Vye are engaged to be married.'

'We are,' Clym answered. 'But we shall not marry for some time yet.'

'I should think not,' Mrs Yeobright replied. 'You will take your wife to Paris, I suppose?'

'No, Mother, I have told you. I am not going back to Paris. I am going to open a school in Budmouth. Eustacia will help me. She is a fine woman and will make me a good wife.'

'If she makes you a good wife, there has never been a bad one!' Mrs Yeobright answered angrily. 'I am your mother, Clym, but you have forgotten your love for me. You think only of her. Why did you come back to bring me nothing but unhappiness?'

'If that is how you feel, I shall marry Eustacia as soon as I find a place for us to live,' Clym replied.

Clym walked out of his mother's house angrily when he had said this. He had planned that Eustacia and his mother should meet that afternoon. He had hoped they would become friends.

He knew now that this was impossible. Clym had to make a choice. He chose Eustacia.

When he met Eustacia later that afternoon, he persuaded her to marry him in two weeks' time. Clym promised Eustacia that he would find a home for them on the heath. They would live there for no more than six months. Then they would move to a house in Budmouth and open their school.

Eustacia agreed. That same evening, Clym packed up his things and prepared to leave his mother's house.

It was June now, but the next day was cold and windy. Clym walked six miles across the heath in the direction of the village of East Egdon. He had seen a small, empty cottage on the other side of the village.

He decided to move into the cottage at once. He could not stay in his mother's house a moment longer. The next day, his things were sent to East Egdon and he arranged to buy some furniture.

'Goodbye, Mother,' Clym said sadly, holding out his hand to Mrs Yeobright. 'Eustacia and I are going to be married on the twenty-fifth of this month. Then you must come and visit us.'

'I don't think I shall ever do that,' Mrs Yeobright replied.

'If you don't, it will not be my fault – or Eustacia's – Mother. Remember that! Goodbye.'

Clym kissed his mother and walked quickly out of her house.

When her son had gone, Mrs Yeobright walked up and down for a long time, crying bitterly.

The day of the wedding came, but Mrs Yeobright did not leave the house. At eleven o'clock, she heard the church bells from far away.

Then the unhappy woman covered her face with her hands.

'Oh, it is a mistake,' she cried. 'Clym will live to regret[3] this day. And then he will think of me!'

12

Lost and Won

When Mrs Yeobright's husband had died, many years before, he had left some gold pieces. They were to be divided between Clym and Thomasin whenever they needed them.

Mrs Yeobright had been made unhappy by the marriages of her son and of her niece. But she was an honest woman and had no thought of keeping the money from them.

On the day of Clym's marriage, Mrs Yeobright took out the gold pieces and counted them. There were exactly one hundred. She divided them into two heaps of fifty and put them carefully into two small bags. She knew that Thomasin would be at Mistover Knap that evening with Clym and Eustacia. Mrs Yeobright did not want Wildeve to know about the money. She did not trust him.

She therefore decided to send the money by Christian Cantle to Mistover Knap. Thomasin would receive her money safely and Clym would have his too.

Mrs Yeobright told Cantle what was in the bags. She made it clear that the money must be given only to Thomasin and Clym.

It was nearly nine o'clock when Cantle left Blooms-End, but it was not yet dark. As soon as he was out of sight of the house, he sat down and took off his boots. Then he put the money from one bag into one boot, and the money from the second bag into the other boot. It was not easy for him to walk but Christian Cantle was sure that the money was completely safe.

Soon after Christian set out, he met a noisy group of villagers on their way to the Quiet Woman inn. They persuaded Christian to go with them.

That evening, the villagers were playing dice[4]. They were playing for a piece of cloth. Every man put a shilling on the table and they threw the dice in turn. Cantle put down his shilling with the others. When he threw the dice, he had the highest number.

When Christian was given the cloth, everyone laughed. The silly young man picked up the dice and held them in his hand.

'Well,' said Christian to Wildeve, who was standing nearby, 'I never knew I was lucky before! I could help a near relation of yours to increase her money.' And he tapped one of his money-filled boots on the floor.

'What do you mean?' Wildeve asked.

'That's a secret. I am taking something from Mrs Yeobright to your wife. That's all I can tell you.'

Wildeve guessed at once that Christian was carrying money to Thomasin. He realised that Mrs Yeobright did not want him to know about it.

'If you are going to Mistover Knap, I'll go with you,' Wildeve said, picking up a lantern. 'Here. Take the dice with you for luck.'

Wildeve and Christian Cantle walked off into the darkness.

A few minutes later, Diggory Venn, the reddleman, got up quietly and left the inn too.

The night was hot and misty and insects flew against the light of the lantern.

45

'So you are carrying money to my wife,' Wildeve said. 'You could have given it to me.'

'No, I've got to give it into Mrs Wildeve's hand, that's certain,' Christian answered quickly.

When the two men had nearly reached Rainbarrow, Wildeve said, 'It's hot tonight. Let's rest here for a while, Christian.'

The men sat down with the lantern between them. Christian put his hand into his pocket and took out the dice.

'What power these little things have!' he said. 'They've made me a lucky man. I was never lucky before.'

'Why, of course you're lucky! You could win more than a piece of cloth tonight,' Wildeve said. 'Let's throw the dice again!'

Wildeve found a large, flat stone and placed it beside the lantern. He took a shilling out of his pocket and Christian did the same.

They played and Christian won, and then he won again. But at the third throw, Wildeve took all the money.

'Why, now I have nothing left!' Christian cried. Then he remembered the money in his boot.

'Why, this money is your wife's, so it's the same as being yours,

Mr Wildeve,' Christian said slowly. 'If I win, your wife will gain. If I lose, she'll have the money anyway!'

Wildeve smiled. He liked the idea of getting Mrs Yeobright's money in his own hands.

Wildeve had already put his gold coin on the stone. The dice were thrown and thrown again. Both men won in turn. They became more and more excited with the game.

Then suddenly, Christian Cantle saw that he had lost all the fifty gold pieces. 'I don't care! I don't care!' he cried, taking off his boot to get at the other fifty.

'Here's another, and maybe I'll win them all back.'

Time went on. Wildeve was as excited as Christian now. He was determined to win all the money Christian was carrying.

It was nearly eleven o'clock when Christian gave a loud cry. He had lost the last coin to Wildeve.

'What shall I do? What shall I do?' he cried out.

'Why worry? The money's mine by right, anyway,' Wildeve said with a laugh.

'No, no, half of the money is for Mr Clym!'

'Then Mrs Yeobright should have given it to Eustacia,' Wildeve replied. 'But it's in my hands now.'

Christian put on his boots. He was so unhappy that he was almost crying. Then he stood up and walked quickly out of sight.

Wildeve realised that it was too late now to go to Mistover Knap. Thomasin would have gone home in Captain Vye's little carriage long before this. He stood up to go back to the Quiet Woman.

Then suddenly, from behind a bush, stepped the tall figure of the reddleman.

———

Wildeve stared at Venn.

'Have you been watching us all the time?' Wildeve asked in surprise.

Venn did not answer. He sat down in Cantle's place and put a piece of money on the stone.

'Put down your money,' the reddleman said. 'Or are you afraid to play with me?'

Wildeve sat down and placed a coin on the stone.

'That money isn't yours,' said Venn.

'It's my wife's,' Wildeve replied. 'And what's hers, is mine!'

'Very well, let's begin.'

The two men began to play without another word. First Venn won, and then Wildeve. Insects flew against the lantern and into the faces of the players. The men took no notice.

Twenty minutes passed and Venn had won sixty gold coins. The game went on.

Venn sat perfectly still. But Wildeve was greatly excited and he could not sit still or control his feelings. At last the end came. Wildeve threw down his last coin and Venn won it. Without a word, <u>Venn gathered up the</u> money and disappeared into the darkness.

Wildeve got up slowly and went towards the road. When he heard the sound of a carriage, he hid behind a bush.

As the open carriage passed, Wildeve saw Eustacia. Next to her sat Clym Yeobright, with his arm round his wife's waist. They were going home to Clym's new cottage.

As Wildeve looked at the woman he had loved and lost, he forgot about the money. Turning sadly in the other direction, he made his way back to the Quiet Woman inn.

Further down the road, Venn heard the carriage too. He stepped out into the road.

'Is that you, Diggory?' Clym asked in surprise. 'You are having a lonely walk!'

'I am waiting for Mrs Wildeve,' the reddleman explained. 'Has she left Mistover yet?'

'No, but she will be coming by here soon.'

Venn waited for half an hour until he saw the lights on

Captain Vye's little carriage. He stepped out into the road.

'I'm sorry to stop you, Mrs Wildeve,' the reddleman said. 'But I have something to give you privately. It's from Mrs Yeobright.' Venn put the hundred gold coins, wrapped in a piece of paper, into Thomasin's hands.

'That's all, ma'am,' he said, and turned away.

So Venn gave Thomasin her own money and the money that was meant for Clym. It was a terrible mistake. Venn did not know that half the money was to be given to Clym.

It was a mistake that was to bring sadness and trouble to many people.

13

'I Will Never See Your Mother Again!'

The July sun shone over Egdon Heath. It was the one time of year when even Eustacia found the heath beautiful. The greens of spring had changed to the bright, rich colours of the flowering heather[4].

Clym and Eustacia were living in their little cottage in perfect happiness. When three weeks had passed, Clym began reading again, for many hours a day.

Eustacia had always believed that she would be able to persuade Clym to take her to Paris. But when she saw how hard Clym was studying, Eustacia became anxious[3]. She did not, however, mention[4] the matter to her husband.

Then about six weeks after her marriage, something happened to make Eustacia speak.

A day or two after Thomasin had received the money from her aunt, she wrote a letter to thank her. Thomasin did not mention how much money she had received. And she said nothing to Wildeve about it. Christian Cantle was too frightened to tell Mrs Yeobright what had happened. Wildeve kept silent too.

Mrs Yeobright began to wonder why she had not received a letter of thanks from Clym.

One morning, Mrs Yeobright heard that Eustacia was visiting her grandfather at Mistover. Mrs Yeobright decided to walk up the hill to see Eustacia and to ask her about the money.

Mrs Yeobright told Christian Cantle where she was going. At last he told her what had happened. All the money had been won from him by Wildeve.

'What! Is he going to keep it all?' Mrs Yeobright cried in anger.

'I hope not!' cried Christian. 'But he said you should have given Clym's share to Eustacia. So perhaps Mr Wildeve has given half of the money to Eustacia himself.'

Mrs Yeobright thought that this had probably happened. It would please Wildeve to give Eustacia the money himself. But she was very angry and hurried off to find out the truth from Eustacia.

Mrs Yeobright started out at two o'clock. She met Eustacia by the pool where so many strange meetings had taken place.

Eustacia stared at Mrs Yeobright as though she was a stranger.

'I have something to ask you . . .' Mrs Yeobright began.

'Indeed!' said Eustacia. 'I did not think you wanted to see me.'

'I am only here on business,' Mrs Yeobright replied coldly. 'Excuse me, but . . . have you received a gift from Thomasin's husband – a gift of money?'

'Money from Mr Wildeve? No – never! What do you mean by that, madam?' Eustacia cried in sudden anger. 'You ought to think better of me than that! Why should I receive money from a

50

man who is not my husband? You have always thought the worst of me!'

'No, no, I was trying to look after Clym,' Mrs Yeobright answered.

'You think that Clym needs to be protected from me?' Eustacia asked with angry tears in her eyes. 'I have not harmed him by marrying him!'

'Well, it is done now,' said Mrs Yeobright in a kinder way. 'I am ready to welcome you as a daughter . . .'

'And yet you think that I take gifts from Mr Wildeve?' Eustacia said proudly. 'I tell you I lowered myself when I became Clym's wife. I love him. But I have no wish to live on Egdon Heath. If I had known we were going to stay here so long, I would never have married him. And now you come here to insult me. And you tried to turn Clym against me before our marriage!'

'It was my duty,' Mrs Yeobright answered. 'I am only a poor old woman who has lost her son. Lost him to a young woman who insults me!'

'If you had treated me well, you would have your son still,' Eustacia cried through her tears. 'But now I can never be friends with you.'

'Take care, Eustacia,' said Mrs Yeobright quietly. 'If you show your temper[3] to my son, you will find he will be very hard on you.'

And Mrs Yeobright turned and walked away, leaving Eustacia crying bitterly by the pool.

———

Eustacia hurried back to her husband's cottage. Her face was still flushed and marked with tears.

'What is the matter, Eustacia?' asked Clym.

Eustacia looked down and said quietly, 'I have seen your mother today and I will never see her again!'

'Why do you say that?'

'Why? Because she says wicked things about me. How could I have taken money from Mr Wildeve? What does your mother think of me?'

'Oh, Clym, we must get away from all this,' Eustacia went on. 'Take me to Paris, Clym! Go back to your old job. I don't care how poor we are, as long as we live in Paris and not on Egdon Heath!'

'But I shall never go back to Paris!' said Clym in surprise.

'You make me very unhappy, Clym,' said Eustacia as she turned away.

The next day, Thomasin paid Clym and Eustacia a hurried visit. She gave Clym the money which she now knew was his. Eustacia was not in the house. Clym told Thomasin how Mrs Yeobright had quarrelled with his wife.

'Never mind, Clym, they may become friends in time,' Thomasin said.

Clym shook his head. 'Not after what has been said,' he answered. 'Neither of them will forget this easily.'

'Well, at least the money has not been lost,' Thomasin said.

'I would rather have lost the money twice over, than have this happen,' Clym replied sadly.

14

The Furze-Cutter

Through all these troubles, Clym was sure of one thing. He had to go on with his plans for the school. He read for many hours during the day and late into the night too.

One morning, Clym woke up with a strange pain in his eyes. He had been reading later than usual the night before. Clym found that he could not look at the light. He wore a bandage over his eyes all day.

Eustacia was very frightened. She sent for a doctor from Anglesbury. The doctor said that Clym's eyes were badly strained. His sight might be in danger.

Clym had to stay in a darkened room, where Eustacia read to him by the light of a shaded lamp[2].

After a few days, the doctor came again. He told Clym that he would have to stay indoors with shaded eyes for a month. He would not be able to read or study for some time.

Eustacia was very unhappy. Paris seemed further away than ever. She often went alone into the garden to cry.

Clym thought at first that he would send for his mother. Then he decided not to worry her. When the doctor came again, he was able to tell Clym that he would not go blind. But his eyes were very weak. He would not be able to read for a very long time. Clym hoped, however, that one day he would open a small school on Egdon Heath.

Clym could walk about now with his eyes shaded. One afternoon, as he was walking slowly across the heath, he met a man cutting furze[1]. Clym recognised the man's voice and stopped to talk to him.

'Now if you had work like mine,' the furze-cutter said, 'you could do a little every day and make enough money to live on.'

'Yes, I could,' Clym said thoughtfully.

When he got home, he said to Eustacia, 'I feel happier today. I think I have found something I can do until my eyes are better again.'

'Yes?' asked Eustacia sadly.

'I can be a furze-cutter. The outdoor work will be good for me. I can earn enough for us to live on.'

Clym did not see the tears rolling down Eustacia's face. She was so ashamed that her husband was going to do this simple work.

The next day, Clym borrowed a cutting hook and heavy clothes. He began to work with the furze-cutter he had met on the heath.

Day after day, Clym got up with the sun and worked until midday. Then after sleeping for an hour or two, he worked again until nine o'clock in the evening.

The man who had come back from Paris was now completely changed. He wore working clothes and dark glasses. Clym was often unhappy when he thought about his mother and Eustacia. But when he was working, he was cheerful and calm.

When Clym was working, he became part of the heath. He could see only the birds, insects and flowers that were close to him. His brown clothes were the same colour as the dying furze.

One warm afternoon, when Eustacia was walking on the heath, she saw her husband at work. To her surprise, Clym was singing a cheerful French song.

It was clear to Eustacia that Clym did not care about his failure. She turned back to the cottage and, when she was alone, cried bitterly.

A few days later, near the end of August, Clym and Eustacia were sitting together at their early dinner. Clym was cheerful, but he could feel his wife's sadness.

'Come, cheer up, dearest,' Clym said. 'Someday, perhaps, I

54

shall see as well as ever. Until then, it is better for me to work. I can't stay at home all day and do nothing.'

'But it is such shameful work! My husband – a furze-cutter! A man who had lived abroad, who can speak French and German!'

'But I refuse to be sad forever, Clym,' Eustacia went on. 'I'm going to enjoy myself this afternoon. Some of the village people are having an outdoor party at East Egdon, and I shall go.'

'To dance?'

'Why not, if you can sing? Are you jealous of my going alone?'

'Well, perhaps I am. But I love you and I want you to be happy. Yes, go. And I will go back to my work.'

When Clym had gone, Eustacia said to herself, Two wasted lives – his and mine. How can I bear it?

Then suddenly she stood up and cried, 'But I will be happy! No one will know how I feel. And I'll begin by going to the dance!'

Eustacia dressed herself carefully and left the house at about five o'clock. Very soon, she could see fifteen or twenty couples already dancing.

But Eustacia did not see anyone she knew. All the people were strangers to her and she decided to walk on.

Eustacia had tea in a nearby cottage and when she returned to the dancing, the sun had gone down. But there was a round moon in the sky and there was plenty of light.

A circle of people was standing around watching the dancers. Eustacia stopped to watch too. She loved dancing and wished she could join the happy couples.

As Eustacia was standing there, someone spoke her name in a quiet voice. She turned quickly to see Wildeve standing behind her. It was the first time they had met since Wildeve's marriage to Thomasin.

'Do you like dancing as much as you used to? Will you dance with me?' Wildeve asked.

'I should enjoy it, but won't it seem strange?'

'Why? Surely, we are relations now? After all, your husband is my wife's cousin. In any case, no one will know you here.'

Wildeve led Eustacia towards the dancers. As they began to dance, Eustacia was filled with new life. She swung round and round on Wildeve's arm, her face full of joy and excitement.

How near she was to Wildeve! She had behaved badly to him, yet here they were, dancing together!

Wildeve had begun to think about Eustacia again, very soon after his marriage. He was a man who always wanted what was not his.

The dance ended. They walked together to a quiet place where Eustacia sat down.

'I was sorry to hear of your husband's illness,' Wildeve said quietly. 'Fate[4] has treated you badly.'

'What do you think of me now that I am a furze-cutter's wife?' Eustacia asked him bitterly.

'I think the same of you as ever, Eustacia. How surprised I was to hear that you were living in a cottage. I thought Clym would take you to Paris at once!'

Eustacia said nothing, but she was almost crying. She stood up slowly and Wildeve went part of the way home with her. Eustacia walked the last part of the journey alone. She soon saw Clym, who was coming to meet her. They walked home together. Eustacia said nothing about her meeting with Wildeve.

15

The Closed Door

Clym had been thinking a lot about his mother. He decided that he must visit her one day soon. Eustacia refused to go to Blooms-End. But she agreed that if Mrs Yeobright came to the house she would welcome her.

Mrs Yeobright was lonely and unhappy. Clym was her only son, and she wanted to be friends with him again. She decided that she would visit the cottage where Clym and Eustacia lived.

It was the last day of August and very hot. Mrs Yeobright left her house at about eleven. The sun was shining brightly.

At the end of the third mile, Mrs Yeobright was very tired. But she was now more than halfway and she decided to go on. She had never been to the cottage before and she had to ask the way.

'Do you see that furze-cutter, ma'am?' the man answered, 'He's going to the same place, follow him.'

Mrs Yeobright slowly followed the furze-cutter who never turned his head. He seemed part of the heath and completely happy there. Suddenly Mrs Yeobright realised that the furze-cutter was her son. She had not known that Clym did this work all day. She was very shocked[3].

Clym went into the house and closed the door. The heat had made Mrs Yeobright very tired by now. She sat down on a little hill overlooking the cottage.

As she sat there, Mrs Yeobright saw a second man walk

towards the garden gate. After waiting for a moment, the man walked through the garden and knocked at the door of the cottage. Mrs Yeobright was too far away to see that the man was Wildeve.

When she heard the knock, Eustacia unlocked the door and opened it.

'I have come to see whether you reached home safely,' Wildeve said, speaking very quietly.

'Of course I did,' Eustacia replied. 'You need not speak so quietly. No one will hear us.'

'Clym isn't at home?'

'Oh, yes. Come in and I'll show you my husband,' Eustacia said with a smile. She locked the front door again and led Wildeve into the living-room.

Clym lay fast asleep on the floor.

'You won't disturb him,' Eustacia said. 'He is very tired. He went out at half past four this morning. I lock the front door so that no one can walk in and wake him.'

The difference between the two men – Clym and Wildeve – was very clear to Eustacia at that moment. Clym was in his working clothes; his face and hands were brown and rough. Wildeve was wearing a new summer suit and a light hat.

'I have nothing to thank Fate for,' Eustacia said bitterly.

'Neither has he. But Fate has given one great gift to him – yourself.'

Eustacia blushed[3] and looked away.

'You belonged to me, Eustacia,' Wildeve went on. 'I did not think I would lose you.'

'You chose another woman,' Eustacia answered quickly. 'I could not bear that.'

'I didn't mean to marry her,' Wildeve said. 'I was playing a game. Clym is lucky. He hasn't lost the woman he loves.'

'Clym is a good man,' Eustacia answered. 'Many women would be happy to have him as a husband. But I want life too –

Clym lay fast asleep on the floor.

poetry, music – all the life of the great world. I thought I could reach it with my Clym. But don't make a mistake – I married him because I loved him.'

Wildeve looked at Eustacia sadly.

'Life now means nothing to me,' he said. 'I have lost the one thing I wanted. And I can never have it now.'

Eustacia was silent for a moment.

'You are saying that you still love me, Damon,' she said. 'I ought not to listen to you, but I cannot help it.'

At that moment, there was a knock at the front door. Eustacia went to the window and looked out. Her face turned very white.

'Who is it?' Wildeve asked quickly. 'Shall I go away?'

'It's Mrs Yeobright. Oh, why has she come here now? She already suspects[3] us!'

'I'll go into the next room.' Wildeve moved quickly away. Eustacia came after him.

'No,' she said. 'If she comes in, she will see you. How can I open the door to her? She wants to see her son, not me.'

Mrs Yeobright knocked again, more loudly.

'Her knocking will wake Clym, and he can let her in himself,' Eustacia said quickly. 'Listen! He is waking up. Come this way, Damon. I'll let you out of the back door. She mustn't see you here. She hates me enough already.'

'Now remember, Damon,' Eustacia added, 'This is your first visit here, and it must be your last. Goodbye.'

'Goodbye,' said Wildeve. 'I have had what I came for – another sight of you.'

Eustacia watched Wildeve until he disappeared over the heath. She was not in a hurry to meet Mrs Yeobright. Clym and his mother could have some time together before she returned.

Eustacia listened for voices, but to her surprise, she could hear none. When she went into the other room, Clym was still fast asleep.

Eustacia hurried to the door, unlocked it and looked out.

There was no one to be seen. In front of Eustacia were the empty path and the open garden gate.

The heath was shining in the heat of the sun. Mrs Yeobright had gone!

16

A Broken-Hearted Woman

Eustacia was worried and unhappy. She sat down beside Clym with a book in her hand, but she could not read.

At about half past two, Clym woke up and said, 'How heavily I have slept! I've had a strange dream too. I thought I took you to my mother's house and when we got there, we couldn't get in. But I could hear my mother crying for help.'

Clym got up and looked out of the window.

'Week after week passes and still mother doesn't come! I can't understand it.'

Eustacia said nothing, but her dark eyes were full of fear.

'I must go to Blooms-End,' Clym went on. 'In fact, I'll walk there this evening. It will be better if I go alone, I think.'

'I don't want you to go tonight,' Eustacia said slowly. 'You may hear something bad about me. Please don't go tonight, Clym.'

'Why should my mother speak against you?' Clym said angrily. 'I want this matter settled[4].'

'Let me go alone tomorrow morning, then,' Eustacia said. 'You could visit her later on. Or I could walk to Blooms-End with you tonight, Clym.'

'No, not tonight, Eustacia. It's too far for you at night.'

Eustacia sighed. 'Very well, then. Do what you want to.' And for the rest of the afternoon, Eustacia sat in a heavy, unhappy silence.

Clym worked in his garden all the afternoon. In the evening, when it was cooler, he set out alone for Blooms-End.

Clym walked on through the calm silence of the heath. Everything was so quiet and peaceful, that Clym began to hope that his visit would be a success. After about three miles, he stopped for a moment to breathe in the sweet scents[4] of the evening.

Meanwhile, Eustacia, alone in the cottage, was feeling more and more unhappy. She wished that she had opened the door to Mrs Yeobright. Eustacia had been certain that Clym would open the door. But she knew Clym would blame her for her mistake.

The evening was cool and pleasant after the heat of the day. Eustacia decided to walk towards Blooms-End to meet Clym on his way home.

When Eustacia was coming out of the garden gate, her grandfather drove by in his little carriage.

'I'm on my way to East Egdon,' Captain Vye called. 'Have you heard the good news about Mr Wildeve?'

'No, what is it?' Eustacia asked in surprise.

'Well, his uncle has died and left him eleven thousand pounds. He heard about it this morning. He's a lucky man! What a fool you were, Eustacia! You married the wrong man.'

Eustacia turned away and said nothing.

'And how's your poor, blind husband?' Captain Vye went on. 'If you want money, I'm willing to help you, you know.'

'Thank you, Grandfather, we have enough,' Eustacia replied.

'Very well. Goodnight.' And Captain Vye drove on.

Eustacia began her walk, thinking about Wildeve and his good fortune. It had been kind of him to say nothing to her about it. He had not laughed at her for refusing to marry him. He had only told her that he still loved her. And she had sent him away!

Eustacia sat down for a moment to think more clearly. She

heard a sound and turned to see Wildeve standing behind her.

'Which way are you walking?' Wildeve asked.

'I am going to meet my husband. I fear I may be in trouble for what happened this afternoon,' Eustacia answered. 'I hear I must congratulate you,' she added.

'Oh, the money you mean,' Wildeve said carelessly. 'I would willingly change my fortune for you. But I can't do that, and so I shall travel. I plan to go to Paris.'

'To Paris,' Eustacia repeated quietly. 'So you will be in Paris, and I shall still be here!'

The two walked on in silence. After about two or three miles, they found themselves near the hill from which Blooms-End could be seen.

'I think you had better leave me here,' Eustacia said. 'People would think it strange if they saw us together.'

'Very well,' Wildeve answered. He took Eustacia's hand and kissed it.

Eustacia looked up the hill and said, 'There is someone in that hut up there. Who is it? Could you walk past there with me?

When they got near to the open hut, they could see the light of a lantern.

A woman lay in the corner of the hut. It was Mrs Yeobright. The doctor from East Egdon was kneeling down beside her. Clym and several other people were standing near by.

'It is my husband and his mother!' Eustacia cried softly, moving into the shadows. 'What can it mean? Is she ill? What is she doing here?'

Wildeve walked quietly round to the back of the hut. Eustacia followed. From the outside, the two listeners could hear every word spoken inside the hut.

'I cannot think where she was going,' Clym was saying. 'She must have walked a long way. But she refuses to tell me where. Is she very ill, doctor?'

'She became very exhausted[4], walking in the heat,' the doctor replied. 'She must have sat down to rest. And then a snake bit her. That has made her much worse. But it is walking in the heat that has made her so ill.'

A woman's voice was heard and there were movements inside the hut.

'That is Thomasin,' Wildeve said quietly. 'They have sent for her too. Mrs Yeobright must be very ill.'

There was no sound except for the heavy breathing of the sick woman. There was a loud gasping sound, and then silence.

Then the doctor said to Clym, 'It is all over. Your mother is dead. Her heart was not strong and the walking killed her.'

Thomasin began to cry. Then a child's voice called out. It was the voice of Johnny Nunsuch. 'Are you her son, master?' he said. 'I have something to tell you. I saw the dead lady this afternoon. She said she was a broken-hearted woman, sent away by her son. She said I must remember and tell you!'

At these words Clym gave a loud cry.

'Sent away by her son! Why did my mother say that? Tell me, Johnny,' he said to the boy, 'where did you see my mother? Was

she going towards my cottage?'

'No, she was coming away,' the boy replied.

'Coming away? No, that can't be true. She did not visit me today.'

'But I saw her there,' Johnny said. 'She was sitting on a little hill. She watched a man going into your house – not you, another man. You had gone in before.' (40)

'What did she do then?'

'She went and knocked at your door. The lady with black hair looked out of the window. But she didn't open the door.'

'Go on,' said Clym in a hard voice. 'What did my mother do then?'

'She turned and left the cottage, walking very fast. I followed her. Her breath made a strange noise and her face was pale.'

'Did you try to help her?' Clym asked.

'Yes, I got her some water from a pool. She told me she had been sent away by her son. Then she went off home.'

'Sent away by her son,' Clym repeated slowly. 'No, Mother, that is not true. Not by your son, but by your son's . . .'

Clym stopped for a moment and then added very quietly, 'May the murderess get the punishment she deserves[3]!' Eustacia.

17

'You Sent Her Away To Die!'

It was early morning by the time Clym Yeobright reached home. He went straight to Eustacia's bedroom. Eustacia was standing in front of the mirror. She saw her husband's face as he came up behind her. It was pale and terrible.

'You know what I am going to say,' Clym said quietly. Eustacia looked up at him, but she said nothing.

'You shut the door. You kept my mother out of my house because you had a man with you. You sent my mother away to die. Tell me that is the truth,' Clym said in a cold, hard voice.

'It is the truth. But the truth is not what you think, Clym.'

'How can it be any different? You were here and you refused to open the door. My mother had come here in kindness. And you kept her out. Did you not pity her?' Clym asked.

'I can explain,' said Eustacia. 'It was a mistake, but I know you won't listen to me.'

'I cannot listen to lies.'

'I'm not lying to you, Clym. I did not open the door because I thought you were awake. I thought you would get up and open the door. I left you to welcome your mother and speak to her yourself. When I saw you were still asleep, it was too late. Your mother had gone!'

'Yes, gone to her death, while you were here with your lover. What is his name? Is it Wildeve? Is it poor Thomasin's husband? What a woman I have married!'

Eustacia began to cry and she fell to the floor at Clym's feet.

'You married a woman who has been faithful[3] to you,' she cried. 'I was happy until we came to live in this lonely place. If I have deceived[3] you, you have deceived me, Clym. I did not want to be the wife of a furze-cutter, here on this terrible heath. I thought that you would take me away, to Paris. To Paris where I would be happy!'

Clym left the room without a word and sat downstairs. The terrible events of the night had exhausted him. He put his head down on the table and slept.

For nearly three weeks after this, Clym was very ill. In his fever, he blamed himself for marrying Eustacia. He blamed himself too for his mother's death. He blamed himself for not visiting her.

He had kept away because of pride and because of his love for Eustacia.

Eustacia stayed with Clym all through his illness. He was too ill to know who she was. But when Clym was better, he was still bitterly angry with his wife. Eustacia decided that they could no longer live together in the same house. She told Clym she would go back to her grandfather.

'Do you really want to leave me?' Clym asked when Eustacia was ready to leave.

'I do.'

'Very well. And when you tell me the name of your lover, I may forgive you.'

Eustacia left the house without another word.

Not long after Eustacia had gone, a villager knocked at the door. 'Yes,' said Clym, 'what is it?'

'I have called, sir, to tell you that Mrs Wildeve has had a baby girl. They are going to call the child Eustacia Clementine.'

What a cruel joke, Clym said to himself when he was alone. That child's name will always remind people of my unhappy marriage.

18

The Last Fire

Eustacia returned to Mistover Knap and her grandfather asked no questions. Her old room was made ready for her. Eustacia lived as she had done before her marriage.

At first, Eustacia never left the house. She did not have the strength to walk and she had no wish to meet people. Charley, who had become Captain Vye's servant, looked after Eustacia. In Charley's eyes, Eustacia was perfect. He did not listen to the stories that were being told about her.

After a few weeks, Clym went back to live at Blooms-End again. When Eustacia heard about this, she felt that her married life was over for ever.

Time passed, and it was the fifth of November once again.

Charley remembered that in past years Eustacia had had a fire at Mistover Knap on 5th November. Charley wanted to please Eustacia. He made a fire in the usual place on the bank above the pool.

Eustacia was sitting indoors with her grandfather. When she saw the fire, she ran to the window.

'What a lot has happened since last year's fire, Eustacia,' Captain Vye said. 'What a lot of trouble you have had! Have you heard from your husband yet?'

'No,' said Eustacia, still looking out of the window. What would Wildeve do if he saw the fire? Would he think it was a sign to him?

Eustacia put on her shawl and went out onto the bank.

'I made the fire for you, ma'am,' Charley said proudly.

'Thank you,' Eustacia answered, 'but you had better put it out now.'

'It will soon burn down,' said Charley.

'Perhaps,' Eustacia answered. 'Leave it then.'

When Charley went back into the house, Eustacia stayed on the bank. As she stood there, she heard a sound she recognised. It was a stone falling into the pool. Then a second stone was thrown. Eustacia moved slowly to the top of the bank and looked down. Wildeve was standing there.

'I didn't light the fire. I didn't call you,' cried Eustacia quickly. 'Don't come any nearer, Damon.'

'You are very unhappy, Eustacia,' Wildeve answered. 'I can see it in your eyes. My poor Eustacia! My poor, poor girl! You have been treated so badly, I think it is killing you.'

'No, no . . .' Eustacia said. Then because Wildeve was sorry for her, she began to cry as though she would never stop.

Wildeve wanted to take her in his arms, but he did not move.

'Oh, Eustacia! Forgive me for the harm I have done you,' he said.

'Not you. Not you. It is the place we live in,' Eustacia replied.

'I think I am partly to blame. But how can I help you? Don't forget, Eustacia, I am a rich man now. Can I bring you anything? Do you want to go anywhere? Do you want to leave this place?'

'We are both married to other people,' Eustacia answered. 'But if you could help me to get away . . .'

'Where do you want to go?'

'Take me as far as Budmouth. I shall go from there to Paris. That's where I want to be.'

'Shall I go with you?' Wildeve asked softly. 'Shall I? Say yes, my sweet.'

Eustacia did not answer.

'Well, let me know when you wish to go,' Wildeve added.

'I will think about it,' Eustacia answered. 'First I have to decide whether you will be my friend or my lover. If I want to go, I shall show a light here one evening at eight o'clock. Then you must be ready to take me to <u>Budmouth</u> at twelve o'clock the same night. When I see you, I shall tell you if I want you to come with me.'

'I will watch for a sign every night at eight,' Wildeve answered. 'When I see the light, I shall get ready to meet you. I will wait for you on the road below Rainbarrow.'

'Very well,' said Eustacia. 'Now please go away. Go away. I cannot bear it any longer.'

Wildeve walked away without another word and Eustacia slowly turned back towards the house.

19

The Sixth of November

All this time, Clym was living at Blooms-End. He was waiting for Eustacia to return to him. He worked in the garden and kept the house tidy in the way that his mother would have wished.

Clym was always listening for sounds of Eustacia's return. But at first, he was determined that he would not ask his wife to come back.

On the fifth of November, Clym thought about Eustacia all day long. Before going to bed that night, he sat down and wrote her a letter.

In the letter, Clym begged Eustacia to come back to him. He promised never to make her unhappy again. He said he would welcome her and love her as before. At the end of the letter, Clym wrote: 'Your husband as ever.'

Clym put the letter on his desk. If she does not come back tomorrow night, he said to himself, I will send this to her.

But he had written the letter too late. By the afternoon of the

70

sixth of November, Eustacia had decided to leave Egdon Heath for ever.

At about four o'clock, she packed up the few things she was going to take with her. Then she sat and waited in her room.

That night, the weather was bad and the sky was covered with heavy clouds. At exactly eight o'clock, Eustacia went out into the stormy night. She lit a small fire on the bank as a sign to Wildeve.

Almost at once, she saw a light from the Quiet Woman. Wildeve had not forgotten her. In four hours, he would be ready to take Eustacia to Budmouth.

Eustacia returned to the house, had her supper and went upstairs to her room. She put out the light and sat in the darkness. Captain Vye sat alone downstairs.

At about ten o'clock, a villager brought a letter for Eustacia. Captain Vye thought the writing was Clym's and he took the letter upstairs at once.

When he saw that Eustacia's room was in darkness, the Captain went downstairs again. He put the letter beside the clock where Eustacia would see it in the morning.

At eleven o'clock, the Captain went to bed. Before getting into bed, he opened the curtains as usual. To his surprise, he saw a light shining from Eustacia's bedroom.

At that moment, he heard Eustacia going downstairs. She was crying softly.

'She is thinking of that husband of hers, silly girl,' Captain Vye said to himself. He got up and called down the stairs.

'Eustacia, Eustacia, there is a letter for you.'

There was no answer and Eustacia did not come back. After five minutes, the captain went downstairs. He was surprised to see that the front door was unlocked. Eustacia must have left the house. How could he follow her? The night was dark and there were many ways she could have taken.

Captain Vye turned back from the door. Then he saw that the letter was still beside the clock.

But the letter had come too late. Even if Eustacia had seen the letter, she would not have changed her mind.

The night was very dark. Rain had begun to fall heavily. Slowly and unhappily, Eustacia made her way towards Rainbarrow.

As she walked through the wind and the rain, Eustacia suddenly realised that she did not have enough money for the journey to Paris.

What could she do? If she took money from Wildeve, she would have to let him go with her.

'Damon Wildeve loves me. But I cannot spend my life with him. I don't love him enough,' Eustacia cried aloud. 'But I have no money. I cannot go alone. What can I do? Why has Fate been so unkind to me? I have tried to be a good woman. But life here has been against me. What can I do?'

The unhappy woman moved down Rainbarrow towards the road. Above the noise of the storm, she heard the sound of rushing water. It was the river running with terrible force over Shadwater Weir[1]. 'Must I go with Wildeve?' Eustacia cried. 'Is that the only way?'

———

While Eustacia was alone on Rainbarrow, Clym was waiting for her at Blooms-End. He was sure that his wife would come to him as soon as she received the letter.

The evening passed. At about eleven o'clock, Clym fell asleep. An hour later, he was awakened by a knock at the door.

'Who's there?' he called.

'Oh, Clym!' cried a woman's voice. 'Please let me in.'

It must be Eustacia, Clym thought as he hurried to the door.

'Thomasin!' he cried when he saw the figure outside. 'Why are you here and where is Eustacia?'

'I don't know where Eustacia is,' Thomasin answered as she came into the house. 'But, oh, Clym, I'm afraid she is with my husband!'

'What!'

'I'm sure they are going away together,' Thomasin said. 'Wildeve went out of the house about an hour ago. He thought I was asleep. I saw him take a lot of money with him. Then I heard him getting the horse ready. I know he met Eustacia last night, because I followed him.'

'Had Wildeve left when you came here?'

'No, Clym. If you hurry, you may be able to stop him. He will listen to you.'

As Clym was getting ready, there was another knock at the door. It was Captain Vye.

'Is my granddaughter here?' the Captain asked.

'No, I don't know where she is,' Clym replied.

'But you ought to know. You are her husband,' the old man answered angrily.

'She's planning to go away with another man,' said Clym. 'Help me to stop her! Come with me now to the Quiet Woman.'

'I am too old to walk any further on a night like this,' Captain Vye replied. 'I'll go back home. There's nothing I can do if Eustacia isn't here.'

The two men left the house together, leaving Thomasin by the fire. Captain Vye took the path to Mistover and Clym went quickly towards the inn.

———

At twenty minutes to twelve, Wildeve led his horse and small carriage from the stable. He walked quietly to a point about a quarter of a mile from the inn. Here Wildeve waited, trying to shelter himself from the heavy rain. Above the noise of the rain, he could hear the water rushing over Shadwater Weir.

After a time, Wildeve looked at his watch. It was a quarter past twelve. At that moment, he heard someone coming.

'Eustacia?' said Wildeve, stepping forward. But the figure standing in the light of the lantern was Clym.

73

'It's you, is it?' Clym cried. 'Where is my wife?'

As he spoke, there was a loud splash from the direction of the weir.

'Good God,' Clym cried. 'Someone has fallen into the water. Is it Eustacia? Bring the lantern and come with me!'

At the foot of the weir, there was a large, round pool. The water was rushing into it with a terrible speed. In the middle of the fast-moving water was a dark shape.

'Oh, my darling!' cried Wildeve. Without taking off his coat, he jumped into the deep water.

Clym waded[4] into the lower part of the pool and began to swim towards Wildeve and Eustacia. Immediately, the three of them were covered by the rushing water.

The two weir-keepers heard the noise and ran out of their cottage with long poles. After some time, the weir-keepers brought out the body of a man. A second man was holding him tightly round the legs. The two bodies were placed on the grass. Soon Eustacia's cold body lay beside them.

The three were taken back to the Quiet Woman inn. Servants were wakened and the doctor was sent for.

Thomasin, who had returned to the inn alone, learnt the sad news first.

Eustacia and Wildeve had been taken out of the water – dead. Only Clym showed some signs of life. All three were taken to the bedrooms upstairs.

As Thomasin sat by the fire, crying and nursing her baby, there was a knock at the door. It was Charley. He had been sent by Captain Vye to find out what had happened to Eustacia.

Charley's face went white when he heard the news. Then he cried out, 'Can I see her once more?'

'You can,' said a voice from the stairs. Clym stood there, thin and pale as a ghost.

'Come and see her, Charley,' he said. 'She looks very beautiful now.'

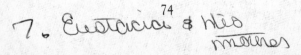
7. Eustacia & his

Without taking off his coat, he jumped into the deep water.

They stood silently, looking down at Eustacia. Her black hair lay round her pale face. She looked very calm and more beautiful than ever before.

On the other bed lay Wildeve. His face too was calm – the face of an intelligent, hopeful, young man.

As they walked from the room, Clym spoke quietly.

'She is the second woman I have killed this year,' he said. 'I was the cause of my mother's death. Then I spoke cruelly to my wife and she left me. When I asked her to come back, it was too late. How I wish that I had died with her!'

20

Afterwards

The story of the deaths of Eustacia and Wildeve was told on Egdon Heath for many months. Their love was talked of by strangers. The lovers were pitied by everyone. But most of all, people felt sorry for Clym Yeobright.

Thomasin mourned[3] for her husband. But she had her child to look after and this calmed her. All Wildeve's money belonged to Thomasin now and she was a rich woman.

Thomasin went to live at Blooms-End, where Clym needed only two small rooms. The new year came and went and Thomasin became happier. Her life was very quiet, but perhaps more pleasant than before.

Clym did not lose his sadness. He spent many hours walking alone on the heath. His mother had left him a little money, and he lived in the simplest way. Clym lived in the same house as his cousin, Thomasin, but he did not have anything to do with her life. He went his own way, thinking his own sad thoughts.

A year and a half passed.

One summer day, Clym was working in the garden. He looked up and saw a young man standing by the gate.

It was Diggory Venn, but he was no longer a reddleman. His face and hands were white now and he was smartly dressed.

Thomasin came to the door and looked at Venn in surprise.

'Is it really you? I don't believe it,' she said with a smile.

'I stopped selling reddle last Christmas,' Venn told her. 'I am a dairy-farmer now, as my father was. I have fifty cows, ma'am.'

'Come in and have some tea, Diggory,' Thomasin said kindly. 'You will not frighten my little girl now.'

After this, Diggory Venn came to Blooms-End quite often. He often met Thomasin when she was walking with her little girl on the heath.

One day, Thomasin told Clym that she was thinking of marrying Venn.

Clym looked surprised, so Thomasin said, 'If I marry anyone, I shall marry him. I cannot leave the heath. It is my home. I know that once my aunt did not want me to marry Diggory. But now he is a man with money.'

'Very well, then,' Clym said with a sad smile. 'If you want to marry him, I cannot stop you. And I hope he will make you happy, Tamsie, my dear.'

And so Thomasin married Diggory Venn at the end of the month.

There was a party after the wedding. Clym was invited, but he did not go. At the end of the evening, the married couple drove off to Venn's house. Clym was alone at Blooms-End again.

Clym Yeobright sat down opposite his mother's old chair. He had never forgotten her. To Clym, Mrs Yeobright still seemed alive. Every day, he wished that he had listened more carefully to her advice.

'Mother, Mother!' he said aloud. 'If only I could live my life again! I would put you first, always.'

Clym did not wish to be a schoolmaster now. He decided to

stay on the heath for the rest of his life and tell the people about God.

On the Sunday following the wedding, Clym went up to the top of Rainbarrow. He stood on the place where Eustacia had stood two and a half years before. Around him sat a small crowd of villagers.

The people listened to Clym because they knew him. Some believed what he said, and some did not. But they all listened to him kindly because they knew the sad story of his life.

POINTS
FOR
UNDERSTANDING

Points for Understanding

1

1 Why were all the children on Egdon Heath afraid of the reddleman?
2 Who did the reddleman see standing on top of Rainbarrow?
3 What did the villagers of Egdon Heath do every year on 5th November?

2

1 What was the name of the inn on the road below Rainbarrow?
2 Who was the landlord of the inn?
3 Why were Thomasin Yeobright and Damon Wildeve not able to get married in Anglebury?
4 Wildeve saw a smaller fire burning on Mistover Knap.
    (a) What strange words did Wildeve say as he looked at the fire?
    (b) What did he do?

3

1 Eustacia Vye said to the boy: 'And if you hear a frog jump in the pool, run and tell me.'
    (a) What did Miss Vye say a frog jumping in the pool was a sign of?
    (b) Why had Miss Vye lit the fire on Mistover Knap?
    (c) What was the sound she was waiting for?
2 Eustacia dreamt of a love that would change her life. How did she want her life to be changed?

4

1 Why did Johnny run back to Mistover Knap?
2 What did the boy see when he got back there?
3 When Johnny told Diggory Venn about the frog, what did Diggory realise immediately?
4 Diggory Venn read a letter by the firelight.
    (a) How old was the letter?
    (b) Who had written it?
    (c) What did the writer say in the letter?
    (d) What did Diggory make up his mind to do?

5 Damon Wildeve said to Eustacia: 'Let us go there together and leave this terrible place.'
  (a) What was the 'terrible place'?
  (b) Where did Damon offer to take Eustacia?
  (c) What was Eustacia's reply?
  (d) Who was listening to this conversation?

5

1 Diggory Venn went and spoke to Eustacia. What did Diggory realise was the difference between Eustacia Vye and Thomasin Yeobright?
2 Diggory spoke to Mrs Yeobright and told her that he wanted to marry Thomasin. What was Mrs Yeobright's reply?
3 Wildeve told Eustacia that she had one week to make up her mind. What did Eustacia have to make her mind up about?
4 'Have you heard the latest news, Eustacia?' said Captain Vye.
  (a) Who was coming to Egdon Heath?
  (b) Where was he coming from?
  (c) What did Eustacia think of this news?

6

1 'Why aren't we friendly with the Yeobrights?' Eustacia asked her grandfather.
  (a) What was Captain Vye's reply?
  (b) Why did Eustacia wish her family were friendly with the Yeobrights?
2 Every Christmas, for hundreds of years, the villagers of Egdon Heath had acted the old mummers' play of St George and the Turkish Knight.
  (a) Why did Charley and the mummers want to use Captain Vye's barn?
  (b) Who took part in the play?
  (c) Where was the play acted?
3 When Eustacia was listening to the mummers talking together, she heard something which made her unhappy. What did she hear?
4 Eustacia asked Charley to do something for her. Charley agreed to do it, but he did not want money.
  (a) What was Eustacia's plan?
  (b) What did Charley want from Eustacia?

7

1 What did Eustacia reply when Clym Yeobright asked her why she had taken part in the mummers' play?
2 What had Eustacia promised to do on the night of Mrs Yeobright's party?
3 Why did Eustacia now wish that Thomasin was married to Wildeve?
4 Eustacia wrote Wildeve a letter.
   (a) What did she say in the letter?
   (b) What did Wildeve do two days after receiving the letter?

8

1 What did Clym Yeobright think of Egdon Heath?
2 What was Clym's new plan? What did his mother think of his plan?
3 Susan Nonsuch pushed a needle into Eustacia's arm when they were in church.
   (a) Why did Susan Nonsuch push the needle into Eustacia's arm?
   (b) What did Clym Yeobright think of such a thing?
4 'Then why don't you come to Mistover Knap with us tonight?' one of the villagers suggested to Clym Yeobright.
   (a) What were the villagers going to do at Mistover Knap?
   (b) What was Clym's reply?
   (c) Why was Clym interested in Eustacia Vye?

9

1 They were sure to meet some time, Mrs Yeobright told herself unhappily.
   (a) Who were sure to meet?
   (b) Why was Mrs Yeobright unhappy?
2 Clym asked Eustacia to help him to teach the villagers of Egdon Heath. What was her reply?
3 Eustacia and Clym both thought very differently about Egdon Heath and about Paris. What was the difference in their attitudes to these two places?
4 Why did Clym walk on the heath in the direction of Mistover Knap?

10

1 Clym Yeobright was determined to start a school on Egdon Heath.
   (a) How did Clym think Eustacia could help him?
   (b) What did Mrs Yeobright say about Eustacia when she heard about Clym's plan?
2 Clym realised that he could not have his three desires together.
   (a) What were his three desires?
   (b) Why could he not have them together?

11

1 Clym had to make a choice.
   (a) What had Clym planned for that afternoon?
   (b) Why was his plan now impossible?
   (c) What choice did Clym make?
2 What did Mrs Yeobright do on the day of Clym's wedding to Eustacia? What did she think of the marriage?

12

1 Mrs Yeobright gave Christian Cantle two bags.
   (a) What was in the bags?
   (b) Who was Christian to give the bags to?
2 'I never knew I was lucky before,' Christian Cantle said to Wildeve.
   (a) Why did Christian think he was lucky?
   (b) What else did Christian say to Wildeve?
   (c) What did Wildeve suggest to Christian?
   (d) What happened to all the money that Christian was carrying?
   (e) Who was watching Christian and Wildeve?
3 What happened next to the money that Wildeve had won from Christian Cantle?
4 What terrible mistake did Diggory Venn make?

13

1 What had Eustacia always believed she would be able to do? Why was she now anxious?

2 Mrs Yeobright asked Eustacia if she had received money from Damon Wildeve.
   (a) What money was Mrs Yeobright referring to?
   (b) Why did Eustacia become angry?
3 'Well, at least the money has not been lost,' Thomasin said to Clym. What was Clym's reply?

14

1 Why did Clym decide to become a furze-cutter?
2 Clym got up with the sun and worked until midday. What did he do in the afternoon?
3 What was Eustacia's reaction when she heard her husband singing cheerfully at work?
4 As Eustacia was standing alone at the outdoor party, someone whispered her name.
   (a) Who was it?
   (b) What did they do together?
   (c) Did Eustacia tell her husband about the meeting?

15

1 Mrs Yeobright sat down on the hill overlooking her son's cottage.
   (a) Why did she sit down?
   (b) What did she see after her son had gone into the cottage?
2 What was Clym doing while Eustacia was talking to Wildeve?
3 'Come this way, Damon. I'll let you out of the back door,' Eustacia said.
   (a) Why did Eustacia not want Mrs Yeobright to see Wildeve?
   (b) What did Eustacia think would happen while she was letting Wildeve out of the back door?
   (c) What in fact happened?

16

1 What happened in Clym's strange dream?
2 What was the good news that Captain Vye had heard about Wildeve?
3 Where was Wildeve now planning to go?

4 'Are you her son, master?' Johnny Nonsuch said to Clym.
   (a) What had Mrs Yeobright told Johnny to say to Clym?
   (b) What had Johnny seen while he was watching Clym's
       cottage?
5 'May the murderess get the punishment she deserves,' Clym
  Yeobright said. Who did he think was the murderess?

17

1 'It is the truth,' Eustacia said to Clym. 'But the truth is not what
  you think.' What did Eustacia mean by this strange remark?
2 Thomasin had a baby girl.
   (a) What name were they going to give to the girl?
   (b) Why did Clym think it was a cruel joke?

18

1 Eustacia ran to the window when she saw the fire.
   (a) Where was the fire?
   (b) Who had made the fire?
   (c) Why had he made it?
   (d) What did Eustacia wonder?
2 'Shall I go with you?' Wildeve asked Eustacia.
   (a) Where did Eustacia ask Wildeve to take her?
   (b) What was Eustacia's reply to Wildeve's question?
   (c) What arrangement did Eustacia make with Wildeve?

19

1 At about ten o'clock, a villager brought a letter for Eustacia.
   (a) Who had written the letter?
   (b) What did the writer say in the letter?
   (c) Where did Captain Vye put the letter for Eustacia?
   (d) Why was the letter too late?
2 Eustacia suddenly realised that she did not have enough money for
  the journey to Paris. Why did she not want to take the money from
  Wildeve?
3 What sound did Eustacia hear above the noise of the storm?
4 'Must I go with Wildeve?' Eustacia cried. 'Is that the only way?'
  What other way could Eustacia have been thinking of?

5 'Why are you here and where is Eustacia?' Clym asked Thomasin. What were Thomasin's replies to Clym's questions?
6 What sound did Clym and Wildeve hear as they stood together on the road below Rainbarrow?
7 Clym Yeobright said: 'She is the second woman I have killed this year.' What two women was he referring to?

20

1 Clym looked up and saw a young man standing by the gate at Blooms-End.
    (a) Who was the young man?
    (b) How had he changed?
    (c) Why had the young man come to Blooms-End?
2 Clym Yeobright no longer wanted to be a schoolmaster.
    (a) What did he decide to do?
    (b) Why did all the villagers listen to him kindly?

GLOSSARY

Glossary

SECTION 1

Terms to do with life on Egdon Heath

Note

Egdon Heath was a lonely place in the south-west of England. The people who lived on Egdon Heath had lived in the same way for hundreds of years. Nothing changed from one year to the next. The people knew each other very well and they did not like strangers.

The people of Egdon Heath did things in the same way their parents and grandparents had done them. And they did special things at certain times of the year – these were their *customs*.

One of their customs was to light fires every year on 5th November. They lit these fires on the highest hills on Egdon Heath. Another custom was to act a play in different houses at Christmas time. The men who acted in the play were called *mummers* and the play was called the *mummers' play*. The mummers wore special *costumes* – clothes worn by actors – and *helmets* which covered their heads and faces. The mummers' play was very old. There were characters who always appeared in the play – The Turkish Knight, Saint George and Father Christmas.

The people of Egdon Heath had many strange beliefs. They believed in *witches* – women who could do harm to people by magic.

Everyone on Egdon Heath had their position in society. There were the *good families* – usually people with money and large houses. The working people were usually poor and lived in small cottages.

costumes (page 24)
> See Note above and illustration on page 27.

custom (page 7)
> See Note above.

dairy-farmer (page 18)
> a farmer who kept cows and sold their milk. Mrs Yeobright did not think that dairy-farmers were of *good family* – see Note above. Thomasin thought that Mrs Yeobright would not allow her to marry Diggory Venn because he was a dairy-farmer.

family – *a good family* (page 9)

    See Note above.

furze (page 53)

    a bush which grows on heathland. Trees did not grow on Egdon Heath and the people used wood of the furze for their fires. A *furze-cutter* is a man who cuts the furze and sells the wood for firewood. The furze is cut with a *cutting hook* – see illustration on page 59.

helmet (page 26)

    See Note above and the illustration on page 27.

inn (page 7)

    a place which sells beer and whisky, etc. The inn in a lonely place like Egdon Heath was also the place where people met and told one another the news of what was happening on the Heath.

mummers (page 24)

    See Note above.

Weir – *Shadwater Weir* (page 72)

    a weir is a dam across a river. There was a deep pool in the river below Shadwater Weir. See the illustration on page 75.

witch (page 33)

    See Note above.

SECTION 2

Terms to do with life in nineteenth-century England

Note

Thomas Hardy, the author of *The Return of the Native*, was born in 1840 and died in 1928. His novels describe life in the late nineteenth century. Many of the things which are referred to are no longer in common use.

bucket (page 34)

    a wooden container used to get water from a well.

lamp – *shaded lamp* (page 53)

    an oil lamp whose glass is covered over with a piece of cloth so that the light is not too bright. Clym Yeobright also had to shade his eyes so that bright light would not hurt them.

lantern (page 7)

a candle inside a glass container. The glass kept the wind away from the candle so that the lantern could be carried out of doors. See the illustration on page 46.

master (page 17)

a way of speaking to a person to show respect. It is similar to the way the word *sir* is used today.

shawl (page 14)

a piece of cloth worn by women to cover the head and the shoulders. See the illustration on page 15.

van (page 6)

a cart pulled by a horse. There was a covering over the cart. See illustration on page 7.

SECTION 3

Terms to do with emotions and personal relationships

anxious (page 49)

worried and unhappy.

blush (page 58)

Eustacia's face became red because Wildeve had said something nice about her.

deceive (page 66)

to tell lies to someone.

deserve (page 65)

to be punished in a way which is as great as the wrong she has done.

disgrace (page 9)

to bring shame on someone by involving them in something which is wrong.

faithful (page 66)

Eustacia is telling Clym that she has been a good wife to him. She has not loved any other men since they were married.

fault – *nobody's fault* (page 9)

no one is to blame for what has happened.

flushed (page 39)

Clym's face was red because he was excited and happy.

insult (page 11)

to do something wrong to someone.

long (page 23)

to want something very much.

mourn (page 76)

to be sad because someone has died.

regret (page 44)

to be sorry because of something you have done. Mrs Yeobright is
sure that Clym's marriage will be unhappy.

shocked (page 57)

unpleasantly surprised.

sigh (page 12)

a sound made by a person's breathing which shows they are
unhappy.

suspect (page 60)

to think that someone is doing something wrong.

temper (page 52)

to let someone see that you can become very angry.

trust (page 9)

to believe that someone is honest and truthful.

unfaithful (page 31)

to be unfaithful is to deceive the person you love by loving
another person.

SECTION 4

General

bandage (page 37)

a piece of cloth used to cover a wound.

barn (page 24)

a large building on a farm used for storing things.

burial-place (page 6)

a piece of ground where dead people are buried.

diamond (page 32)

a very expensive stone used in jewellery.

dice – *play dice* (page 45)

to gamble by throwing six-sided cubes with numbers on each side.
See illustration on page 46.

elderly (page 7)

becoming old.

exhausted (page 63)

.very, very tired.

fate (page 56)

what happens to a person in life is their fate.

gracefully (page 9)

smoothly, like a dancer.

heather (page 49)

a plant which grows on heathland.

knows – *God knows* (page 14)

words used to emphasise what you are saying.

landlord (page 9)

the man who keeps an inn.

licence – *marriage licence* (page 11)

an official paper which says that a man and a woman can be married.

mention (page 49)

to tell someone about something.

mind – *never mind* (page 40)

do not think about.

niece (page 8)

the daughter of your brother or sister is your niece.

practise (page 24)

before a play is acted, the actors go through the play many times. To practise something is to repeat it many times so that you can do it well.

scents (page 62)

sweet, pleasant smells of flowers.

settle – *I want this matter settled* (page 61)

to settle a matter is to talk about it and make a decision. Clym wants to talk to his mother and make friends with Eustacia. This is the matter to be settled.

sign (pages 13 and 14)

something which tells you what is going to happen. Also, a signal made by arrangement. Eustacia's fire is a sign to Wildeve that she is waiting for him.

telescope (page 12)

an instrument which enables you to see clearly something which is far away from you.

wade (page 74)
    to walk into water.
wasted – *to be wasted* (page 33)
    Mrs Yeobright thought that her son could do better in life than
    be a schoolmaster.

Of Mice and Men *by John Steinbeck*
Bleak House *by Charles Dickens*
The Great Ponds *by Elechi Amadi*
Rebecca *by Daphne du Maurier*
Our Mutual Friend *by Charles Dickens*
The Grapes of Wrath *by John Steinbeck*
The Return of the Native *by Thomas Hardy*
Weep Not, Child *by Ngũgĩ wa Thiong'o*
Precious Bane *by Mary Webb*
Mine Boy *by Peter Abrahams*

For further information on the full selection of Readers
at all five levels in the series, please refer to the
Heinemann Guided Readers catalogue.

Heinemann English Language Teaching
A division of Heinemann Publishers (Oxford) Ltd
Halley Court, Jordan Hill, Oxford OX2 8EJ

OXFORD MADRID ATHENS PARIS FLORENCE PRAGUE
SÃO PAULO CHICAGO MELBOURNE AUCKLAND
SINGAPORE TOKYO GABORONE
JOHANNESBURG PORTSMOUTH (NH) IBADAN

ISBN 0 435 27266 7

This retold version for Heinemann Guided Readers
© Margaret Tarner 1979, 1992
First published 1979
Reprinted five times
This edition published 1992

Illustrated by Jenny Thorne
Typography by Adrian Hodgkins
Cover by Shirley Barker and Threefold Design
Typeset in 10.5/12.5 pt Goudy
by Joshua Associates Ltd, Oxford
Printed and bound in Malta by Interprint Limited

95 96 97 10 9 8 7 6 5 4